Charlie Bird
Elizabeth Carty
Vincent de Veau
David Deegan
Katie Donovan
Bishop Martin Drennan
Paul Durcan
Anne Enright
Frank Feely
Norman Fischer
Hayley Fox Roberts
Sheena Furlong
Ann Henning Jocelyn

Rita Ann Higgins
Rose Mary Logue
Richard Marsh
Geraldine Mills
Seán Moncrieff
Rábbi Julia Neuberger
Eibhín Nic Eochaidh
Rita Normanly
Mary O'Malley
Joe O'Shea
John O'Shea
Colin O'Sullivan
Jonathan Philbin Bowman

Jack Preger
David Rice
Mary Rieke Murphy
John W Sexton
John Seymour
Eamonn Sweeney
Colm Tóibín
Brian Trench
Paolo Tullio
Dick Warner
Mike Watts
Jenny Wheatley
Mary P Wilkinson

A LIVING
WORD

A LIVING
WORD

COMPILED BY JACQUI CORCORAN

TOWN
HOUSE
DUBLIN

First published in 2001 by
TownHouse and CountryHouse Ltd
Trinity House
Charleston Road
Ranelagh
Dublin 6
Ireland

1 3 5 7 9 10 8 6 4 2

A CIP catalogue record for this book is available from the British
Library.

ISBN: 1 86059 146 9

Cover illustration detail from *Intrusion* by Gerald Davis
(Private collection, Dublin)
Cover design: Terry Foley
Typeset: Claire Rourke
Printed in Finland by WS Bookwell

Contents

INTRODUCTION

It all started with a meeting with my boss. I was relocating to the Waterford studio. It was a personal choice; I'd had enough of the madness of living in Dublin city centre and it was time to get myself and my son to the countryside. RTÉ was mercifully supportive of my quest. My first assignments: to produce a series of money-advice programmes with Colm Rapple, and to take over production of *A Living Word*.

I was vaguely horrified at the prospect. *"Money and the God Slot? But I'm a financial disaster area,"* I explained, *"and I'd hardly qualify on the religious front either." "You're a producer,"* my boss retorted. *"You're a programme-maker. Make the programmes work."* After a lengthy meeting I headed home, my head buzzing with ideas. I couldn't wait to get stuck in.

It is now over three years since I started producing *A Living Word*. In the midst of the very wide variety of projects I have worked on over that time, it is the one that is closest to my heart. It has been my job to develop the slot and broaden it into a daily broadcast that has some relevance to today's listeners. It has become a personal journey of sorts. A fulfilling experience that has (I hope) broadened my own thinking and influenced my outlook on life.

There are wonderful moments, such as those when I read a script that leaves me gobsmacked: like the heart-wrenching reality of motherhood expressed in Ann Henning Jocelyn's piece on her air-emergency experience; or Richard Marsh's story of the brother-to-sister blood transfusion; or John W Sexton's poignant, evocative reflection on the death of his friend.

The relationships I have developed with many of my regular contributors have been important. I have made many friends; and that closeness is something I like to see reflected in the pieces I choose for broadcast. I think it is important for the contributors to have a sort of intimacy with the listener for those brief moments of the broadcast, and sometimes for longer. I follow my instincts; trying to strike a balance and open my mind to different viewpoints while taking on board the horrible responsibility I carry in having to decide which pieces to reject from the hundreds of contributors who send me scripts. It makes my job difficult at times.

There is no episode that stands out in my memory of producing *A Living Word* as much as the experience of recording Jonathan Philbin Bowman's contributions. When I initially approached him, he was somewhat surprised that I thought he would be a suitable contributor, but he relished the challenge and promised to get working on scripts. After a few days he called with the suggestion that he try *ad libbing* the five pieces. Twenty-five excellent pieces later, he left the studio. Three days later he died. The shock of the news was so, so terrible for so many people. Listening to the pieces selected for broadcast the following week was heart-breaking, but also, I know, of some comfort to his family, friends and others. If the slot manages, as in that instance, to reach out to people in some way, then I am happy in my work.

I like to think that *A Living Word* has moved on from its old nickname, that it is no longer 'The God Slot' and is about many more things than *religion* in the narrow sense. I strive to commission and accept scripts from a broad range of contributors with a broad range of opinion, style and background. I don't expect every listener to agree with or like every contribution, but I do try to maintain a quality in the standard of writing and presentation that will make people pause for a few moments and simply listen. Whether I succeed in this pursuit is up to listeners, and readers, to decide.

This book contains a selection of contributions to *A Living Word*. The collection comprises a number of commissioned scripts and also selections from the many new writers who send me their work.

I would like to say a very sincere thank you to those who have helped with this project, especially everyone at TownHouse and, of course, all the authors who have allowed their work to be broadcast and now published.

Jacqui Corcoran
JULY 2001

CHARLIE BIRD

1

JOURNALISM is a funny business; one day you can be reporting on a political or financial crisis, the next on a disaster of one kind or another. People often ask me what the biggest story I ever reported on was and I surprise them when I say the Stardust fire tragedy of 1981. At the time, I hardly knew where Artane was, but over the years I have passed close to the spot on many occasions and the memories of that terrible night come flooding back. Forty-eight young people died in the Valentine's night disco fire. I can still see the image of a fireman trying to break through the window filmed by the RTÉ cameraman.

At first light on the Saturday morning, a group of journalists were led through the charred remains of the disco. In the hours that followed we interviewed some of the survivors, the relatives and friends of those who perished. In the following days came the procession of funerals. Since then I've occasionally met some of the relatives of those who died. No doubt the intervening years have helped heal some of the bitter memories of that awful night.

Sometimes we forget that, when the cameras move away from a story, there are real people who have to live with their grief and their loss. Behind every disaster, every tragedy, there are real people.

2

O N the 23rd of February 1993, a young Irish nurse was killed in Somalia, thousands of miles from her home in Dublin. At the time, her tragic death was a major news story. The bloody civil war in Somalia and its aftermath, which led to a major famine in that part of Africa, grabbed world headlines for many months. Valerie Place was a staff nurse at St James's Hospital in Dublin. She'd volunteered to work with the aid agency Concern at their feeding station in Mogadishu at the height of the famine. As their convoy was making its way from Mogadishu to Baidoa it was fired upon and Valerie was killed.

Over the years hundreds, if not thousands, of young Irish people have given up their time and energy, working in some of the most difficult and dangerous places in the world for organisations like Goal, Concern, Trócaire, The Red Cross, Refugee Trust, World Vision and APSO. Some of these volunteers lost their lives to disease and accidents. Over the years we've had a proud tradition of helping people far away from our own shores. To all of those who have worked in the various trouble spots around the world, often placing themselves in great danger, we owe a debt of gratitude.

3

SOMETIMES, as a journalist, there are those rare moments when you feel a sense of history or a sense of presence. There are few people, for instance, who have been in the company of Nelson Mandela who will not tell you that the man, who spent almost 30 years in captivity, exudes a unique aura. Even from a distance, you know you have been in the presence of someone rather special.

Here at home there have been a number of occasions when you get a feeling of a sense of history in the making. The troubled birth of the Good Friday Agreement was one of those moments. At the height of the Drumcree stand-off three years ago, Richard, Mark and Jason Quinn were burnt to death in their council home in Ballymoney in north Antrim. I can remember standing outside the burnt-out remains of their house on that Sunday morning in the pouring rain with other reporters and camera crews huddled together. The confirmation by the RUC mid-morning that the three young children died as the result of a sectarian attack seemed, at just that moment, to have drained the tension from right across the north of Ireland. Despite the awfulness of what happened, it seemed as if their deaths had not been completely in vain.

4

A REMARKABLE event happened a few weeks ago, but it was almost completely overshadowed by the dramatic outcome to the US presidential election. It was Bill Clinton's visit to Vietnam. The image of a US president being officially welcomed to Hanoi was, by any standards, an extraordinary event. As a child of the sixties, one could not forget the nightly images on our television screens of the bombing of Vietnam – the B52 bombers disgorging their huge pay loads, the helicopter gunships. And who could forget the image of that young child running down the road after being burnt by a napalm bomb?

It is hard to believe that those two adversaries could ever end their quarrel. Over 50,000 Americans lost their lives in the Vietnam War. Between 2 and 3 million Vietnamese from both sides were killed. But today a new Vietnam has emerged. It is now one of the most popular holiday destination spots in the Far East. In the week that Bill Clinton returns to our shores, hopefully the lesson of Vietnam can be learned here at home. No matter how deep the scars or how deep the wounds, people can forgive.

5

THE uninhabited part of Inisheer, the smallest of the Aran Islands off the Galway and Clare coast, looks out onto the broad Atlantic and the Cliffs of Moher. Save for the black-and-white painted lighthouse, which stands tall and dark against the sea and the limestone rocks, and which has been there for almost 150 years, the view which one sees from the back of the island probably hasn't changed much in over a thousand years. On a winter's day, one might come across an islander out collecting the *slata mhara*, the sea sticks. In the summertime, if you look out towards the Cliffs of Moher, you might see a tiny *currach* bobbing up and down as the fisherman hauls in his lobster-pot. Here you can sit on the rocks and take time out from the madness of the world. There isn't a soul I have met who hasn't come away filled with a sense of spirituality. Thankfully there are still many places with this unique quality around our country. We should treasure and enjoy them.

ELIZABETH CARTY

1

BEEZIE was my grandmother's cousin. She had never married; rumour had it that she had been disappointed in love. She wore dull, crossover aprons and wrinkled grey lisle stockings and her hair, coarse as sheep-wire, was stapled with black hairpins. She criticised constantly and passed judgement on everything. *"You are bad-mannered and spoiled,"* she said, *"and bone idle into the bargain."* We avoided her like the plague. She was the wicked witch of the fairytales – as sour as a crab-apple.

I was getting ready for my 18th birthday party when she arrived uninvited, with a gift, an ancient wristwatch on a bracelet of gold. *"You'll have no excuse now for staying out half the night and putting the heart crossways in your poor mother."* I thanked her in amazement; Beezie never gave presents to anyone. She was outraged at the sight of my strapless silk dress and high-heeled sandals. *"No decent girl would go out in a dress like that."* She said that I'd break my neck and catch my death of cold. *"I was the best looking girl in the parish at 18,"* she observed tartly. *"There was them used to say you'd stand in the snow to watch me dance."* My brother sniggered, starting us all off. She turned and left, white-faced and silent. It was the only time I have ever seen my mother truly angry.

My father and I cleared out her small house after she died. There wasn't much, just some old clothes and a few bits of worm-eaten furniture. I found the picture in a drawer, stuck in an old prayer book. A young girl in a flowered dress, her black curls tossing on her shoulders. Wearing my watch on one slender wrist. Her dark eyes laughing out at me. And I could almost imagine the young men watching her. Beezie – dancing in the snow.

2

IN the Cavan countryside where I grew up, there was no such thing as a stranger. Our house was never empty; the kettle was always boiling. We knew everybody, everybody knew us. Our family, like most of those around us, had lived there for generations. As children we dreaded second mass on summer Sundays. There was always some returned Yank, it seemed, to pinch our cheeks painfully and comment on our family likenesses and enquire after our parents without even having to ask us our names.

When I got married and moved to another part of the country, I didn't really miss at all the constant comings and goings, the gossip, or the complete lack of family privacy that had been part of my childhood. But I also hated the fact that in my new parish I was a stranger. Neither myself nor my husband had any links with the area, our roots here went back no further than 10 years earlier when the children had first started school. Loneliness was a problem but a greater one still was a sense of not belonging. My old home had been sold when my mother died. I had never met the new owners. There was no going back and nothing to go back to.

My children grew up and went to secondary school and it seemed as if another tenuous link had been severed. But then, coming out of mass one Sunday, a small boy rushed against me in pursuit of a friend, almost knocking me over. I learned later that he was the nephew of our near neighbour. I had never met his parents but I recognised him long before then, by the shape of his mouth, the dark curls that fell across his forehead in an unruly tangle. The wheel had turned full circle and I had finally come home.

3

THE only person, living or dead, that our elderly neighbour, Pat, held a grudge against was St Swithun. He was outraged that an arch-villain had reached sainthood despite the fact that he invariably sent torrents of rain on his feast day, thus ensuring not only 40 days of bad weather but the guaranteed loss of every grain of hay in the parish besides.

Pat considered everyone else's house to be an extension of his own. When we younger people brought guests home he would walk in, unannounced, and demand to know their name, birthplace and occupation, and whether their fathers had good jobs and money in the bank. Most of them found his childlike curiosity inoffensive and highly amusing. I remember my mother, at his wake, saying with unaccustomed sternness, *"He never said a wrong word about anyone. It's no crime to be interested in your neighbours."*

Recently a black couple moved into the neighbourhood. The locals are cautious. Someone asked me half-laughingly, *"I wonder what Pat would have made of them?"* I could have told them. He'd have walked in, probably unannounced, and demanded to know their names and where they came from, what they worked at, how many children they had. He would have filled them in on the treachery of St Swithun, advised them on the early sowing of spuds and the right way to set a blackthorn hedge. Like my mother said, he was interested in the neighbours.

4

ABOUT 10 years ago, a woman approached my stall at a craft fair and asked me to make a patchwork quilt for her only daughter. She already had the fabrics, she said. She had been saving them for years. The girl had just become engaged to an Australian, and, after her marriage, she would live there with her new husband. We arranged an appointment and some weeks later she arrived on my doorstep, dragging two large plastic sacks. She tipped the contents without ceremony in the middle of my workroom floor and began to sort through them, lovingly folding and stroking each piece as she told me their story.

They each marked a chapter in the life of her daughter. The blue taffeta was from her Debs and the heavy, green serge from her first school uniform. The sprigged muslin was from a Miss Muffett costume; it had won her first prize in a fancy dress competition the year she was eight. There was pink silk from a bridesmaid's dress, which she hated, but she had been wearing it when she first met her future husband. The faded blue-and-white stripes were from her bedroom curtains, the polka-dot cotton from the apron of a much-loved doll.

Separately, the fabrics were beautiful, but together I feared they would be a disaster. I tried to explain this, but at the look of utter devastation on the mother's face I sighed and promised, against my better judgement, to at least attempt what she was asking. Four months later, the finished result went to Australia, a mish-mash of colours and textures that had miraculously come together and blended harmoniously into a work of absolute love.

I think of her sometimes, that young woman whom I've never met, waking up on the other side of the world under a kaleido-scope of memories that had been hoarded so lovingly by her mother down through the years.

5

THE kitchen of the small country shop where I grew up was a meeting place for everyone. The young men gathered there on their way to dances or football matches, the old ones to gossip or play cards, youngsters to plot fishing trips and childish mischief. Saturday afternoons, though, belonged to the women. Countrywomen like my mother, they were busy with farm work and their large families, with little time for themselves. But on Saturday afternoons they'd arrive and, while she filled their bags from their shopping lists that were written on the backs of old envelopes, they'd sit in the warm kitchen and drink tea and catch up on the news. They gossiped a little, discussed the merits of a new government or a new hairdresser, or shared their pride in their children's triumphs in this strange new world of free education. None of them had ever gone beyond National School, but they were intelligent and articulate and fiercely interested in the world around them. Some of the local wags dubbed these Saturday meetings the 'Holy Hour'.

The week after my mother died we held the last one, a sombre affair at which we talked little and sipped tea between heavy silences. And some time afterwards the shop was sold, and life moved on, and we with it. And now we live in a different, fast-moving modern world where, despite ever more sophisticated methods of communication, we are becoming increasingly isolated and alienated from each other. Loneliness is a disease of our time. And I think of the Saturdays long ago, and these women with their sense of affinity and belonging, taking the time out from a busy week for a Holy Hour in which to share in each other's lives.

VINCENT DEVEAU

1

WORKING as the editor of a magazine is a pretty good job, and most of the time I enjoy it. The most satisfying and most difficult part of it is also, paradoxically, the simplest: choosing what we'll print and what we won't, what works and what doesn't. In a recent issue, we ran a photo feature about people and their dogs. It proved, to judge by the response, a success with our readers, and it also proved a success with my nine-year-old son, which is more amazing than anything else. He's grown rather blasé about anything the old man does, apart from pitching baseballs to him – he's inherited my New York Mets fanaticism – or buying him Pokémon paraphernalia or accompanying him to James Bond movies. This time, though, he was genuinely enthralled, and asked me loads of questions about the article, including this one: Why hadn't I put him and his dog into the magazine? Little did he know how much I'd thought about it.

You see, my son actually has two dogs: one lives with him and his mother, the other lives with me.

The breakdown of a marriage leaves a lot of wreckage in its wake of course, but, more importantly, it leaves a lot of anomalies for a little boy to handle: two separate and distinct parents, two houses, two bedrooms, two sets of toys, two ways of being in the world and, in my son's case, two dogs.

The editor saw a perfect opportunity. He's a good-looking kid, if I say so myself, and smart as a whip. A photograph of him playing in a field with both of his very different dogs would be lovely, and I knew he could be counted upon to say some very interesting things on the subject to the right interviewer. It was a natural. I thought about it for days, and in the end, thank God, I didn't do it.

What the editor found so attractive, the father finally shrank from in fear. And I have been thinking ever since about just what it was that I was afraid of. Did I not want to draw his attention to this anomaly, to focus his mind on these symbols of the two different sides of his life? If so, I was kidding myself. He knows all about it, and what he thinks and feels – though I try to be the best father I know how to be, though I try to listen even to what is unsaid – I still cannot fully fathom. Perhaps I didn't want to draw my *own* attention to it. This seems more likely, because I stand before him a failure in what mattered most, and, more often than I admit, even to myself, a coward. I worry constantly about what he feels, and yet I am afraid to know. In years to come, as men, I imagine we will talk about it. Someday. But not today. Today I am grateful to watch him ducking and diving in the tall grass of Phoenix Park with Maggie, the little collie who lives with me. And I am grateful for the stories he brings me about Dick the dachshund, the faithful friend who lives with him in another place, no longer mine. I will try to be ready to answer his questions, when he asks them, and I will keep vigilant for signs of the questions he does not yet know how to ask. I will do the best I can. And the magazine will have to do without that picture.

2

A S we approach the last days of the Clinton administration, I'm reminded with pleasure of my tiny, fleeting brush
with it, and I shall mark its passing with more than a little
regret. During his last visit to this island, I spent a day following Mr Clinton around a rain-sodden Dublin. It was good craic
on the press bus, and, even if the earth didn't exactly move, it
was still a great show. I had been, however distantly and briefly,
near the mountaintop and had got a decent look around. It
would suffice for a dinner party conversation or two.

And then my cellphone rang.

Now, here I have to be a bit discreet, changing the names to
protect the innocent, so to speak. You see, a friend of a friend of
a cousin of a brother-in-law of my great-aunt's next-door neighbour – approximately – just happens to be related to someone
very well placed in the White House – and, said the voice on the
other end of my phone, if I hopped in my car and drove like the
clappers to Ballybunion the next morning, I just might get to
meet the President of the United States. It's a very American
way of doing things, this friend-of-a-friend business, and, as it
happens, a very Irish one, too. It's no wonder we get on so well.
Anyway, flash-forward a few hours, and there I am in
Ballybunion – in my best dark blue, double-breasted, weddings-
and-funerals suit, waiting in the bar of the Ballybunion Golf
Club for the President to come off the 18th. What happens next
is a bit of a blur, I have to admit. What I do remember is that as
Mr Clinton approached – radiating 24-carat, 100-megawatt,
weapons-grade charisma – my critical faculties shifted into neutral and my emotional age dropped from forty-something to eight-
and-a-half. I'm not proud it, I don't know why it happened, but
there it is. Clinton, in person, is made of phosphorous. We're
talking about serious star-power. And, if you think about that,
superficial observation though it may be, it actually helps to
explain a lot about what went wrong with his presidency and,
in the end, what didn't.

I did manage to have a conversation (using the term very loosely) with the President, and I'd like to take this opportunity to record for prosperity the substance of our consultations, so that this precious moment is not lost in the subsequent rush of history. It went something like this:

"Hi," said Mr Clinton.

"It's a pleasure to meet you, Mr President," I replied.

"Do you know what day it is?" the leader of the free world enquired.

"I beg your pardon, sir?"

"Is today the 5th?" the President asked.

"Yes, sir, I believe it's the 5th," I responded with all the gravitas I could muster.

"Thanks," said the President.

"Thank you, Mr President," I replied.

What was all that about? I have absolutely no idea. But I headed straight for the bar and ordered a large one, and then chased it with another. And I imagine I shall someday tell my grandchildren about those 20 seconds or so, and that, by then, my brief encounter with the President of the United States will have acquired considerably more breadth and depth. In the meantime, I'd learned a little something about how the aura of power and the spell of charisma can reduce an otherwise reasonable adult to the condition of a gibbering chimpanzee. It's worth knowing.

And like I said: Thank you, Mr President.

3

LOVE, it seems to me, having danced its dance a time or two, is not a state of being, but an ambition. An act of hope, not a possession. A journey, and not a destination. If it were otherwise, we who dance that dance would not need to dance so desperately nor so often, nor would we regret so bitterly the dances fate has left us to sit out, nor would we fall to the floor with such a crash each time we miss a step.

When one is in love, of course, such distinctions are meaningless, and the sober counsel of others falls on deaf ears. The experience of that love seems infinite, all-encompassing, inexhaustible, inevitable.

Those of us who stand outside know this is not, and cannot, be true, but the exaltations of love still serve to define our own ambitions, to give shape to our hope, and courage on our way.

William Shakespeare's 116th sonnet expresses, perhaps as perfectly as the English language ever has, the experience – and the ambition – of love. I first encountered it many years ago, and though I have forgotten many things since then and would not like to face again the many good teachers who dragged me, kicking and screaming, through Elizabethan diction, I have never managed to forget this sonnet, no matter how often I have fallen short of its mark.

> Let me not to the marriage of true minds
> Admit impediments. Love is not love
> Which alters when it alteration finds,
> Or bends with the remover to remove:
> O no, it is an ever fixèd mark
> That looks on tempests and is never shaken;
> It is the star to every wand'ring bark,
> Whose worth's unknown, although his height be taken.
> Love's not Time's fool, though rosy lips and cheeks
> Within his bending sickle's compass come;
> Love alters not with his brief hours and weeks,
> But bears it out even to the edge of doom.
> > If this be error and upon me proved,
> > I never writ, nor no man ever loved.

4

I AM the child of parents who lived through the Great Depression. I lived through the sixties. The distance between those two experiences, and the sense of possibility they offer, is impossible to overstate. For my parents, the world was an enormous and perhaps even a frightening place. They were born, married and raised their small family within the boroughs of the City of New York, inside a circumference of a few miles. I, on the other hand, first came to Europe when I was 17. I have visited more countries than I can count, and I have long since lost track of the number of times I have crossed the Atlantic.

My father served in the Second World War, but never left American soil, and he died without ever having travelled beyond the borders of his own country. To my great regret, I was of no use to him in that regard.

With my mother, who is still living, I resolved not to make the same mistake. She has visited me several times here in Ireland, and this past year we visited Paris and Rome together. She was amazed and delighted by everything she saw and touched and smelled and tasted. I took a photograph of her standing in the middle of the Champs-Elysées and, although it was the end of a long and tiring day for her, in the picture she looks just like a girl.

She adored Paris, but Rome, unquestionably, was her favourite. My mother is a devout Catholic, and our visit to St Peter's would have been the realisation of a lifelong dream, if ever she had dared to dream it. As it happened, luck was with us, and she was able to see and hear the Pope speak, and, equally fortuitously, we happened to be present when mass was being celebrated at the altar beneath the magnificent Throne of St Peter. Communion was offered, and, with a look of amazement that she was indeed here and that this was really happening, she turned to me and silently indicated that she would like to receive the sacrament.

I'll digress here a moment to explain that the Church and I parted company a long time ago. I take no pleasure in saying that. I perceive that parting as a great loss, and wonder if I shall ever find a way to fill, if not bridge, that painful gap. I am still looking. Meanwhile, I have not received the sacraments since I was a boy, and I have stood aside many times at weddings and funerals to let others pass to the communion rail.

Back in St Peter's, given the size and press of the crowd and my mother's sometimes unsteady gait, I decided that I should accompany her to the altar, offering an arm for support. I had not, however, figured on the consequences. As we arrived before the priest, my mother received the sacrament and, before I could lead her away, the priest drew the obvious conclusion from my presence there and said, "*Corpus Christi*," while extending the host.

A number of possibilities flashed through my mind in that moment, including saying, "*No, grazie*," which seemed, at the very least, inappropriate. I had a choice before me, sacrilege or churlishness, but, before I could make it, the altar boy of 30 years earlier spoke with my voice, inexplicably replying, "*Deo gratias*," and the deed was done.

So, where does that leave me? If a strict interpretation of Catholic doctrine does indeed hold sway in the life hereafter, I'm done for. If it is Allah or Yahweh that I meet, I may have even bigger problems. (If the Buddhists have it right, I just get sent back to screw things up all over again, which doesn't really get us anywhere.) My best hope is if I can offer that picture of my mother on the Champs-Elysées in evidence. For that, as for so many things, I really do say *Deo gratias* – or would, if I could somehow remember how to believe that anyone is listening. I'm working on it.

DAVID DEEGAN

1

1987, entering the great gates of St John's College, Waterford. Wandering into the unknown – and, yes, it was wandering. Just out of school, the daunting task was to find the answer to my father's eternal question, *"What do you want to be when you grow up?"* I used to mutter to myself, *"I don't want to grow up."* But after long conversations with several priests I decided to join up. So in I went. Interesting experience to say the least.

I found that, after a year of St John's College, my interest in the priesthood was dwindling. Morning prayers, midday mass, evening prayer. It was all a bit too much structure for a spirit such as mine. Thirteen years later, having had several careers and planning many new ones for the future, I find life a wonderful and forever changing challenge. Every day has a twist, all for a reason which I accept and enjoy. All through our lives we face change, whether it be in career, family, health or whatever. Learning to embrace change can be a truly rewarding experience, as my life has shown me.

2

NO two human beings are the same. We are all built in our own unique and individual way. Sharing many likenesses with others, but never exact copies, that is why we are all so interesting as people. We are not all alike and we should not expect others to have the same view, perspectives or outlooks on life and living. Sometimes we are selective of whom we talk to and mix with so as not to tarnish our oh-so-delicate image. But sweeping that aside, we can find that talking and interacting with people gives us a greater understanding of ourselves. Trying to accept others for all they are and all they are not, and they, us, for the same reasons, is a great challenge. It is a challenge that is beyond nobody to overcome.

3

SOME years ago I was told about a beautiful island in Yugoslavia called Rab, so one day I decided I was going there. It was a hellish 10-hour bus ride from Munich where I was living at the time, but when I got to the island it was absolutely amazing. I had left the snow-filled streets in Munich and was now in the sun. I took a walk by the harbour. Two ladies standing on the quay looked at me in my hiking boots and haversack as if I was from Mars. They were dressed in rags. I tried to speak to them to tell them that I needed a place to stay but the language barrier made it difficult. They signalled for me to follow them. So on I went through the lanes to their home. These impoverished people took me in, fed me as best they could and put me up. We stayed up early into the morning talking and trying to make ourselves understood. They had so little in material terms but they shared all they had with me. What they gave me was priceless.

4

WHEN I was 18, I was employed for the summer as a life-guard in Ardmore, County Waterford. One Friday afternoon the red flags were up and the rain was coming down in sheets. Suddenly a man ran towards me shouting that there was a 12-year-old drowning at the other end of the beach. I ran the length of the beach to where I found the child. He was not breathing. I immediately started cardiopulmonary resuscitation and mouth-to-mouth resuscitation. I will never forget the scene. A wide circle of onlookers and the child's parents gathered around us. The angry waves crashed against the rocks and a dark sky hung over the scene. I continued CPR. On and on I went, struggling to get some response from the child. Somewhere in the surreal haze around me I could hear the rosary being said. Twenty-five minutes of resuscitation on the boy and there was still no sign of life. I had to stop. Exhausted and distressed I stood up. *"Jesus Christ,"* I said to myself, *"you cannot take this child's life now."* I got back down on my knees and made one more compression on the child's chest. He started to splutter.

KATIE DONOVAN

1

L AST April I went on a pilgrimage to Brazil. I am not a religious person, but I am a curious person; and there are times when I crave mystery.

I went with a group of Irish people, some of them very sick. We travelled for many hours in planes and buses to a village in central Brazil called Abadiania. There, three days a week, the healer João Teixeira de Faria sees all visitors, first come first served. Some are given operations without anaesthetic. Others are given invisible operations or herbal medicine.

I had seen João performing operations on a video before I left Ireland. It was an amazing sight. He hypnotised people and whipped out tumours with a scalpel. There was hardly any blood. His patients came to soon after, with neat little scars, feeling fine.

When I first saw him performing these operations with my own eyes, I thought I was going to faint, but my fascination kept me on my wavering feet. He operates quickly and matter-of-factly, like any doctor doing what has to be done with the minimum of fuss.

João is psychic. He has had very little education himself, but he can channel the expertise of over 30 deceased physicians and herbalists. People come from all over South America to see him, and from as far afield as Australia and South Africa. People with cancer, motor neurone disease, lupus, strokes, MS. Children paralysed or handicapped, brought by their parents. Old people in wheelchairs. Young people on crutches. Rich women with gold jewellery. Working men in creased and dirty jeans.

I received an invisible operation and was prescribed herbal medicine. I cannot say that I felt very much during the operation except some flutterings in my duodenum, where I used to suffer from an ulcer. For two weeks after, however, I felt vulnerable and faint. Six months after my visit, my health has improved and stress does not now automatically make itself felt where I had the ulcer. The other people in the group who travelled with me have reported various levels of improvement.

João does not claim to be a miracle worker. Not everyone who goes to see him is cured. What he can give is often not what people expect. What he gave me, a weary agnostic, was a renewed belief in mystery.

2

WITH the end of the 20th century in view, I have been writing articles for *The Irish Times* on each of its 10 decades. Summing up so many momentous events in short paragraphs is enough to make anyone tear out their hair. But, after letting off steam over the impossibility of it all, I have found myself laughing, crying, stunned with either admiration or horror, or simply baffled. From the Charleston to the Holocaust, there has been no end of ingenuity, tragedy and folly.

One thread runs throughout that gives me pause for thought. The 20th century has truly been the machine age. Starting with the invention of the car and the aeroplane, the century went on to produce nuclear power, the computer, spacecraft travel to the moon, and the global village of the internet.

Before the 20th century, people rarely left home unless there was a calamity or no work. Most of the world's population lived in village communities and worked on the land. Now the world is a predominantly urban place, and we commute across oceans, either strapped into an aeroplane or by turning on our computers.

All of this has made life more convenient, more manageable, more possible. And yet words like 'stress' and 'alienation' are unique to our time. Ironically the machines we have invented to bring people closer together, across continents and time bands, have brought access, but not necessarily intimacy. Talking into a mobile phone while you simultaneously do your shopping in a busy supermarket may be more immediate than writing a letter, but it is far less intimate.

The moon landing was an amazing achievement and, thanks to television, millions of people were able to see Neil Armstrong and Buzz Aldrin take their momentous steps. But it made us see the earth from a new point of view, as a finite, vulnerable place, a place we could detach ourselves from. Detachment strikes out empathy. It means we believe the news-speak that tells us bombs are being dropped but no-one is being killed. It means we are unmoved when we hear that tigers are nearing the edge of extinction as their wild jungles become our cityscapes.

Our young people now prefer to dance to the music of a machine. There is only one person on the stage, to operate the machine. There are no musical instruments, no lyrics, no human voices. It is hardly surprising then that the young need to take pills as they dance, to give them a feeling of intimacy, to reach across to another person, so close and so far away, for a human embrace.

3

I FIND it difficult to strike a balance between respecting an other person and respecting myself, between giving others what they want and getting what *I* want too. In contemporary 'New Age speak', I have issues with my boundaries.

The messages are confusing. As a girl, I have been brought up in the traditional way, to be polite, deferential and kind. Confusingly, as a woman in her thirties, I have also been told it's better to be ambitious and assertive, to walk on other people before they walk on you.

Because I am Irish, I know how important it is to show people a warm welcome, to be witty, friendly and accommodating, and not to lose my temper. Because I am a country person living in the city, I know the value of showing tolerance and acceptance to those who come from very different backgrounds. Because I am a shrewd person, I know that, even if I am sorely tempted to show my anger, it will not necessarily get me what I want.

All of this conditioning comes into play when, either literally or metaphorically, someone steps on my foot. My instant reaction is that my stomach contracts, my fists clench, and I'm ready for a fight. They've invaded my space and carelessly hurt me. I want to protect myself and reassert my boundaries. What I actually end up doing is a different story.

My cats go through similar dilemmas. Every day they mark their territory and retire to survey it from strategic vantage points. When I hear a guttural yowl I know that some other cat has crossed the boundary. It isn't always easy. If a neighbour's dog appears, my cats run away. If they are feeling lazy and contented, they may choose to ignore a trespasser in favour of lolling in the sun.

Boundaries are the chief source of conflict on the planet. All wars are fought over different interpretations of where boundaries begin and end. If war is averted, it is usually because the powers involved are in a lazy contented mood, a bit like my cats in the sun. If a point needs to be scored due to insecurity over territory, then the guns come out, the yowls escalate.

So I keep working on my boundaries. I reckon, if I can sort them out, get my timing right and retreat for a contented snooze in the sun, it's a small step towards balancing the planet.

BISHOP MARTIN DRENNAN

1

WHEN does morning begin? In a story that comes from the East, this is the question that the master puts to his disciples. He gets many answers. One person says the morning begins when the lights are switched on in houses, another suggests that when the cock crows morning has arrived, another takes the view that morning begins when people go out to work. Finally, the master shook his head in disappointment. None of the responses found his approval. So he gave his own view. *"Morning begins,"* he said, *"when we see in each other people for whom we have responsibility. That is when the light breaks through the darkness."*

We are asked to take responsibility for one another. Others depend on us, rely on us, need our support. When we sense that, we have begun to take responsibility.

In the presence of a really good person I don't feel judged or criticised. Instead, the good person gives me back my best self, draws out the good in me. To take responsibility is to help others become their best selves, to let the light push back the darkness of fear and negativity. In this jubilee year, we remember that our God is a God of life, a God who forgives us, sets us free and enables us to live in a way that sets others free. In God there is no darkness, only light. For those who meet this God of light, morning has begun.

2

WHAT comes to mind this morning is a scene from a film where a wealthy businessman comes out of a hotel and makes his way over to his car. As he approaches he sees a poor black boy walking around the car and wonders if the boy is trying to break into it. The boy is only admiring and he says, *"That's a beautiful car you've got."* *"Yes, it is,"* says the business-man. *"Actually, it is a gift from my brother."* The boy says, *"I wish I could be a brother like that."* I expected him to say that he wished he *had* such a generous brother, but no, his wish was to *be* a brother like the one the man had.

A bit curious, the man let the boy into his car and drove around to the apartment where the boy lived. They went up to the flat together and there the man understood what he had heard. The boy's younger brother had been struck down with polio while very young. He was paralysed down one side and could not speak. His brother was truly grateful for what he had, deeply respectful of handicap and illness, and longed to be really gen-erous to his brother who had many needs.

He was a boy who seemed poor, but in reality was rich because he was so free within. He was gifted with the freedom that we thank God for giving us this jubilee year. To be like him is to be free to give thanks for what we have, to be respectful of the limitations of others, and to know we are privileged when we can share what God has entrusted to us.

3

THE gospel figure of Zaccheus is known to many: the story of his meeting with Jesus at Jericho where the experience of being forgiven led him to want to 'unlive' his past greed through a life of generosity.

Less well known is a legend about him. After his meeting with Jesus, he used to leave his house every morning and return about an hour later. One day his wife followed at a distance to see where he went. Zaccheus returned to the tree from which Jesus had called him, poured a bucket of water at the foot of the tree, spent some time in silent prayer and then left for home. When he got back his wife asked what was the meaning of his actions. *"I go back to water the memories,"* he said.

At the tree outside Jericho he had been healed of a painful past, his dignity had been restored. Having met a generous God in Jesus he felt a strong desire to be generous. That event had been a real turning-point in his life. The meeting with Jesus had changed him and he was determined not to let die the gift he had received. So, he decided to give time each day to water the memories, to keep alive the experience that filled him with peace, with joy and generosity. The wise person knows how important it is each day to make space to go back to the wells and there to water the memories.

4

THERE'S an ancient legend that comes to us from the Philippines, a story about a king who had two sons. He wasn't sure which of them was most suitable to succeed him as king so he got some wise people to devise a test. The sons were told that what they were to do was to fill the largest hall in the palace in any way they chose. They had 36 hours to complete the task.

One went to the sugar-cane fields and hired some workers to fill the hall with sugar-cane. When the task was finished he came to his father and said, *"The hall is full; I deserve to be appointed king."* *"Let's wait and see what your brother will do,"* said the king. The hall was emptied and the second son went in and lit a tiny candle on the floor. The light filled the whole hall. The king said, *"You shall be king in my place because what my people need is light."*

We need light in many forms. According to St John of the Cross, *"Creatures do not satisfy our thirst"*; they increase it. We thirst to have our dignity respected, long to understand our experience, to have our hurts healed, to feel good about our lives. Yearning makes the heart deep. Good friendships *do* have a healing effect, but our deepest thirst can be satisfied only by God. His light illuminates all the halls in our hearts.

5

IN his book *The God of Surprises*, Gerard Hughes suggests an exercise where you look down a long roadway and ask yourself the questions, *"What do I want to be when I get to the end of the road? How do I want to be remembered when life is over?"* His point is that, if I want to be a certain kind of person when I come to the end of life, then I need to give direction to my life now, to take decisions that shape the future and make sure I arrive at my goal.

A jubilee year is a good time to take stock of where I am. The way that the Jewish people shaped the laws for the jubilee year makes it clear that they wanted those laws to bring them to greater freedom. They began their jubilee year by asking God for His forgiveness so that they would be free of guilt for past actions. In that year slaves were to be freed and land restored to its owners. People were to be given their freedom so that they could live as God wanted. Freedom from slavery was to become freedom to live for God.

The Archbishop of Dublin has rededicated the diocese to the Sacred Heart of Jesus. In doing so, he was asking us to put our trust in the kindness and mercy of God as we journey through life and to trust that His mercy will bring us to the great destiny that God has in store for us.

PAUL DURCAN

1

I AM having these thoughts in a bath in a hotel in San Francisco. I am here in this strange city to give a poetry recital. It's a luxury staying in a hotel but the great bonus is getting to have a bath. Not having a bath back home in Dublin, I travel to foreign cities not only with all the usual exotic expectations but with the expectation and dream of having a bath. Of course I cut a ludicrous specimen stretched out here in my hot, foaming bath in Room 903 in the Renaissance Park Hotel on Cyril Magnin Street in downtown San Francisco. But that's only a small part of the picture, the image of this ludicrous specimen floating about scrubbing and splashing. The significant aspect of the story is the thanksgiving for this bath. How seriously fortunate a creature is to be stretched out and disporting oneself in hot water, idly, floppily, with the door open. I snuggle right back down and immerse my shoulder blades.

All you regular bath-takers, I ask you never take for granted your daily bath. When I get to have a bath I praise the day that is in it and give thanks for water. Hot and cold.

2

I AM having a hot bath in a hotel in San Francisco. But I wouldn't be having it were it not for the existence of aeroplanes and air traffic control towers. In a world that is so relentlessly, overwhelmingly evil – wars everywhere, famines, meanness, selfishness, egotism, greed, all that universal cult of thoughtlessness – it is surely extraordinary to behold the spectacle of civil aviation. At this very moment there are thousands upon thousands upon thousands of aeroplanes circling the globe. And all of them criss-crossing and interconnecting and all of them completely and utterly dependent on the thousands of control towers located in every corner of the world. What amazing co-operation. What amazing good fellowship. I like flying, not only the delight of take-off and landing, not only the marvellous tranquillity of cruising at 36 thousand feet, but most of all I love the thought, the constantly surprising thought, of all these thousands and thousands of air pilots and all these thousands and thousands of air traffic controllers engaged in this international congress of sympathetic co-operation . If there are really any saints among the human species, chief among them are air pilots and air traffic controllers.

3

HAVING a bath in a hotel in San Francisco and recognising that I wouldn't be here but for the miracle of air transport, I cry eureka as I suddenly realise also and again that the only history is the history of transport. All the ghastly rest of it, politics and war, is but the sordid footnote to the history of transport. The horse, the camel, the chariot, the cart, the canoe, the currach, the ship, the train, the plane, the bicycle, the car: that's the only history worth telling. The only story. Even in my own little life, the crucial moment, if there was a crucial moment, was when at the age of 47 I learned to drive a motorcar. A friend offered to teach me and a year later with the test under my belt I bought a car, the only thing I've ever owned in my life, and I was free. A free man. I felt like a housewife set free after 30 years' captivity. Driving the streets and suburbs, the hills and valleys of my native land at my own pace and own time. Nipping across Dublin to visit my mother or my daughter and not having to wait all day in the rain for four buses that might never come. Driving around Achill Island at 25 miles per hour and getting a slow puncture and pulling in for a pitstop to Teddy Lavelle's Wheels o' Wheels. Sweet liberty.

4

HAVING a hot bath in a hotel in downtown San Francisco, I am watching my toes. Counting them, yes, but also watching them. Toes. Such strange, independent little creatures. No two toes the same. Gazing at them as into the flames of a fire. I see in them the different countries of the world that my work has taken me to and I give thanks not only for my amazing toes, without which I would have had no life, but also for those strange and different countries I have had the good fortune to work in. Here in the great cities of the USA and in Brazil, Australia, New Zealand, Israel, Sweden, Russia, Armenia, Japan.

In Tokyo meeting a young woman from north Mayo who was primary school teaching in a remote village in the Japanese countryside. Nora Kennedy, I said to myself, this is surely what life is all about: mixing it in far distant places and having the innocence as well as the courage to mix it. And there on a street corner at night in Tokyo in October 1998 I had a vision of Ireland in the 21st century, a place to which young Japanese would come and work and live and play and marry. Yes marry! And Brazilians too and Armenians and Russians and Swedes. And the tyranny of the one pure island race would be exchanged for the freedom and beauty and justice of the mixture and the island would walk with a divine energy.

5

TIME to get out of the hot bath in this downtown San Francisco hotel. Of course I don't want to get out, but work and the day are calling. I am in my element in bath water. Of the four elements, water is the holiest. Watching young Dublin boys bathing in the canal lock at Charlemont Bridge, Gerard Manley Hopkins asked, *"What is water?"*

"Spousal love," he answered. Spousal love. In the last 50 seconds of my bath the water is espousing me and I am espousing the water. The water is espousing my ankles, my thighs, my elbows. With my two big toes I espouse the two taps with the one spout. The perfect espousal. A little bit more of hot, a bit more of cold. One last time I immerse and sink and kick and splash. And water is not only spousal, water is innocent, water is generous, water is forgiving. And only innocence and generosity and forgiveness in the end are of any interest. There is only one subject: water. Singing, I pull out the plug. Singing in the bath. A perfect marriage. *"Hey, Mr Tambourine Man, play a song for me, in the jingle-jangle morning I'll come following you."*

ANNE ENRIGHT

1

THESE days, I can only manage being Irish for an hour or so
at a time. When I am abroad, and make an extra effort, I can
be Irish all night long; I can drink whiskey and look sentimental. But it is a strain. And what a comfort to get back to the hotel.

Mind you, I also get tired of being a woman, which involves all
kinds of fakery. People making assumptions. Like that you'll
laugh at their jokes, or flirt. Of course, you mostly do. There
isn't so much difference, is there? Between being a woman and
being an Irish person abroad? Like women, the Irish are irrational, seductive, not to be trusted. Like women, the Irish are
romantic, they are sexually shy, they have wild and secret hearts.
They get paid less.

But being a stage Celt, rather than a stage woman, seems a bit
more fun. You get to drink more and fight in the street. And
then there's all that singing. Most of all you get to say, *"These
days it's all different. These days we make money and shop a lot.
These days we are in charge, or at least not underfoot. These days we
are normal."*

I wonder how long it will last?

2

R EMEMBER when the whole country used to argue about sex? And it was in the news, all the time? And the news-readers were stumbling over words they had never said before, like 'contraceptive device'. The innocence of it.

In the good old days, in the 1980s, no Christmas dinner was complete without a decent barney about a new law or another referendum, and, if you managed to steer clear of abortion, no one ended up crying into the dishes. But divorce! Now *there* was a prime Christmas subject. Finding out that your brother was a fascist or your sister a pure hussy. The surprise of it. The betrayal. The fact that you grew up suddenly. And got over it by New Year's Day.

These days, all the country can fight about is money. Corrupt politicians, fat lawyers. The place is awash, not just with cash, but the secrets of cash. Dublin has a new hotel on every corner. It's all Beamers and my eye.

I suppose we argue about money because it looks like people are making it all the time. They are making money day and night. So what does that say about the 1980s and sex?

3

THE mystery about the Irish is why people from other countries like us so much? You may say that it is because we are
a very nice nation, but I have my doubts. Of course we are a fun-
loving, well-meaning, full-hearted bunch of people. We are generous, warm, witty, wise, poetic, pragmatic, cute, clever and sur-
prisingly intelligent. We are fond, foolish, showy, shy and tal-
ented beyond measure. We are feisty, sentimental, brilliant, nostalgic, highly verbal and only drunk in the best possible taste.
We are, without doubt and above all, great craic. Wild, untram-
melled and unfailingly courteous, we have more than our share
of nature's gentlemen.

But is this enough? Of course, I forgot the great dancing, the
huge hearts of our sporting professionals, in failure as in
triumph. Enormous hearts, humongous, great, big, thumping,
gorgeous hearts, the biggest, tastiest, bravest hearts in the world.

But, for St Patrick's Day, I thought I might remind you that there
are other countries in the world. Consider the Swedes. Lovely
people, the Swedes. I wouldn't hear a word said against them.
Very clean. And who is their national saint? Answers please
on a postcard.

4

IFOUND myself getting all nostalgic the other day. This was a bit of a shock. It seems that there are two generations of nostalgia in Ireland. The first happened in the sixties; it was all doodeens and súgán chairs, all tweed underpants and diddly-di. And I, for one, had nothing to do with it.

How embarrassing then to be part of the second wave. I know these things happen. I know they happen in times of great change. But you would think I could pick something better to be nostalgic about than a row of three-bedroomed, semi-detached houses.

You walk down the street these days and all you can see are the house prices, and you think, *"Remember the days when people actually had gardens? Remember the days when ordinary people lived in Phibsboro?"* And money? Well no one had any money of course, but they had houses. Houses worth gazillions of pounds. Oh, remember when 25 minutes was an awfully long journey into town? When you moved so far out that there wasn't a bus route, and you felt like it was the middle of nowhere? And now it's Terenure.

Remember how boring it was? How utterly, mind-breakingly tedious? And you didn't know that you were blessed?

5

A LOT of Irish books are set in the past. They are not set in the 'real' Ireland, the country full of hotels with buffed-steel counters and flower arrangements that could eat you. They deal with poverty and rain and none of the characters have rings in their navels. This would be depressing were it not for the fact that most books are about the past. And most books, of course, are untrue.

So our immediate history is sold all over the world in all its glorious misery. And people are miffed. They say it was never like that. Of course it wasn't. All writers are liars. We lie our way to the truth. And sometimes do it well.

But still people get involved. They treat the writing game like it is theirs. They get drunk and tell you that you should put the record straight. Or, more gratifyingly, that another writer is rubbish, that they are going wrong, that they are obsessed by childhood, or shouldn't be allowed to write about sex. They act like the supporters of a wayward football team. Which is great, of course. (Though two years spent writing a book is a very long, slow shot at goal.)

FRANK FEELY

1

MR Joyce lived nearby. Thomas Dudley didn't. They had one thing in common. In each case the appearance belied the reality.

Mr Joyce, who was new to the neighbourhood, was always impeccably dressed. He set off each morning, on his bicycle, to what we assumed was an important executive position in the city. Imagine our astonishment when we discovered that he spent his days traversing the city and pausing at various locations. Here he would take out a stick of white chalk and draw a large shamrock on the pavement. On one leaf he would write *"love"*, on a second *"joy"* and on the third *"peace"*. He would then give a short pacifist sermon. From the day of our discovery he was known as Love, Joy and Peace.

Thomas Dudley did not match Mr Joyce's sartorial elegance. He spent his days jumping on and off the rear open platforms of double-decker buses. He would pull a large key from his pocket and point it at passers-by shouting, *"Bang Bang!"* He was a very well-known character and most people would humour him by staggering as if shot. Amazingly Bang Bang (for so he was universally known) was in receipt of a Blind Pension. This likeable character, who had the dexterity to leap onto moving buses, suffered from the eye disease glaucoma.

The moral? Don't judge a person by his or her appearance.

2

I RECENTLY came across a quotation from the American poet Sylvia Plath who had such a tragic life and committed suicide in 1963. *"You are afraid,"* she said, *"of being alone with your own mind."*

In what may seem like a *non-sequitur*, I immediately thought of the Great Blasket island, off the coast of Kerry. The population never numbered more than 300. They were very much alone, often cut off for long periods from teacher, priest and doctor. Their lives were a struggle to eke out an existence from the barren soil and the treacherous ocean. Often on the verge of starvation, they had to come to terms with the loss of life of loved ones to the rugged cliffs or the hungry sea. They bid adieu to sons, daughters, brothers and sisters, never to be seen again in many cases, who were lured to America by the prospect of a life without hunger and deprivation.

Yet with indomitable spirit the islanders made the most of what little they had. Amazingly they produced a bevy of acclaimed writers. Tomás Ó Criomhthain, Peig Sayers and Muiris Ó Súilleabháin are the best known. They wrote movingly of everyday life and of the traditions and the superstitions of the island. In 1953, the remaining inhabitants were moved to the mainland.

These hardy islanders are a good example of the resilience of the human mind when deprived of excessive stimulation. O'Criomhan was not too far wrong when he said, *"You will not see our likes again."*

Perhaps in the hurly-burly of modern life we should make an effort to be alone more often with our own minds.

3

IT seems to me that it is only in recent years that our young people generally have displayed the confidence which their abilities merit.

I recall watching American teenagers marching in St Patrick's Day parades over many years. All pearly white teeth, deeply tanned and with perfect postures they marched as if they owned the world, high kicking their way up O'Connell Street. By comparison our own youngsters appeared to slouch along as if affected by some national inferiority complex. This contrast was symptomatic of the lack of confidence generally of our young people at the time. It probably had much to do with the memories of less affluent days and a more closed society.

I found myself pondering recently on the changes which have taken place over the years. No longer, it seems, do our youngsters generally lack self-confidence. And why should they? On the international scene they have excelled in business, sport, films and academia. In the entertainment world, they have reached heights previously regarded as unattainable. They have gained respect abroad for their concern for the underprivileged and for their general demeanour. It is important that we continue to endeavour to inspire this confidence in young people, particularly those from less-privileged backgrounds. A confident person is more likely to make a success of their chosen career.

4

HE stood in Castle Street in Dublin on a Sunday morning, when the city was at its quietest.

The silence was broken by the joyous sounds of the bells of Christchurch Cathedral pealing out over the inner city. He spoke to an old man sitting on the steps of number 16.

"Aren't the bells lovely, my good man."

"Wha'?"

"I said, aren't the bells lovely?"

"I can't hear you with dem oul bells."

Another example of incongruous sound was when I was awakened with a start very early one morning. Annoyed at the loss of a good night's sleep to which I had been looking forward, I suddenly realised what had awakened me. It was the dawn chorus. It seemed as if every bird in the greater Dublin area had congregated in my back garden to join in the Hallelujah chorus or whatever is the equivalent in birdland. How would they like it, I thought with the twisted logic of an insomniac, if I climbed the trees in my pyjamas and sang "Dublin in the Rare Oul Times" at the top of my voice when they were asleep in their nests.

I always enjoyed hearing Jimmy Durante sing, *"You've got to start off each day with a song even when things go wrong."* But there is a time and place for everything. Sounds, however attractive in their proper settings, can be jarring at other times.

As the Psalm says:

"All things have their season, and in their times all things pass under heaven – a time to keep silence and a time to speak."

NORMAN FISCHER

1

Be present, not tense.

WHAT'S it like to actually be present? And aren't we always present anyway? Well no, not really. Fact is, we are usually half asleep and our brains are full of bits and pieces of desire, dream, delirium, day's and night's detritus. Fact is, the world's a constant astonishment. A blade of grass yearns toward heaven's light, a rose drips morning dew, your loved one's face is radiant with love's glow, but who sees such stuff? It is always here, but we're too busy, too burdened by all we think we have to do. Instead of being present we are tense. We think being present means we have to do something. Actually being present is really about returning, turning around our mind and heart.

It may take some work, this kind of work: take a breath, right now as you are reading these words, take a breath. Breathe in the whole world, and breathe out all your concerns. Let it all go – whatever you think you need or want, that you think you lack – let all of that go when you gently breathe out. Right now, try it.

Let it all go. See what it's like to be here naked, without any of it. Well that's being present. What needs to be done, get done, and what you don't get done, well it didn't need to happen. Being alive is like that; no one gets out of here with his boots on. Recognise this now, this moment, every moment, and you will feel a deep calm.

2

The world we speak about
We would be without
If we didn't speak.

Y AK yak yak. Everyone's always talking – even before there
was an information age, even before a printing press, even
when there was hardly anything to say, there was all this talk
talk talk.

I have been developing the theory that talk is our job; that somehow the world (and I mean the world) depends on it. Fish gotta
swim, birds gotta fly and we gotta talk.

Not that our talk is more important, or more exalted or even
more sensible, than fish swimming or birds flying. It's just another version of the same thing.

What would that do to your talk, what would it do to your
whole approach to life to imagine that being human was not
necessarily the big deal it has been made out to be; at least not
any bigger a deal than the stars in the sky. (Imagine the pattern
of the stars on a pitch dark night in summer. Don't they make a
kind of conversation, with its own syntax and grammar?) It's
not that looking at it like that would make us more humble –
quite the opposite.

A bird isn't humble, not at all, when he puffs up his chest and
sings a song for the whole world. No, this bird figures he's the
centre of the universe and that everything out there needs to
hear his trills, the most beautiful there ever were.

Us too. Once we get in scale with things, once we let ourselves
play with things, maybe we can see our talk for the beautiful
thing that it is, the world itself come alive.

3

What waste of self if your me is only you;
There's plenty of room; include others too.
How big are you anyway: how many worlds do you
*   contain?*

SOMEHOW we have allowed ourselves to be convinced that we are fairly small, much smaller than we are. Truth is, we're not that small. As Whitman said, *"I am large, I contain multitudes, and we're all that way."*

Let go of all that baggage somebody handed you a long time ago: the valise of ego, the duffle-bag of self, the hard suitcase of personality, accomplishment, driven-ness. That's all the same stuff. Be instead large. Contain multitudes. Things are happening everywhere, life is going on and it goes on in me and outside me and through me, and it's all me.

It's my choice. I can hold onto all the baggage and stagger through the airport and miss the boat. Or I can let it go and open myself to the wonder that everything that happens everywhere is mine. And if I can live that way – if I can find kindness everywhere, and can give kindness any time, not worrying so much about what this little guy needs but giving everything away all the time – then for sure my me will get taken care of in the course of things, and all my giving away and giving up will get me happy. Sages have said this in a million ways. We all know about it. Does anyone out there have the nerve to live it?

4

The solution is here; the problem is there.
There are plenty of problems.
You could say it's all a problem; living's
no end of problems.

SO you need to make a switch. Stop looking at what's out
there coming in on you and look at what's inside of you
coming up and falling away. I don't mean bury your head in
the pillow, withdraw and ignore, I mean keep your eyes open –
but look, rather than elsewhere or over there, right here where
you are. Look at your own reactions to what is happening.
Look at how anger feels, study frustration, become an expert
witness to your own fear, lust, confusion. See that your life as
you actually live it is about your *reactions* to stuff, not so much
about the stuff itself.

(This by the way is the real secret about money; it's not what
you buy, it's the mind and heart that appreciates, or doesn't,
what's been bought.) In other words, we live right here, on the
boundary between inside and outside. But inside is where we
have control, power, choice, and inside is where all the action
is. Inside, if you pay attention, if you open up, is where things
lighten up. Where all the fun is. Sure there are problems, plenty
of them. No end to problems. And sure there's no end to what
we have to do to take care of all those problems. But why is that
a problem? Be who and where you are. Enjoy your life. Be in it.
Enjoy your problems.

5

There is nothing more hypnotic
Than one's own point of view
A cure for this – this is the trick:
Be View in lieu of You.

SOMEBODY once said, *"You are what you eat."* I'd say you are
what you think; you are your opinions. Where do they come
from? How do the passions we hold in our minds and mouths
get to be there? What's the difference between a prejudice and
an opinion?

I always get stuck on this point: do I really know what I'm talking about? And when I ask myself that honestly, the answer
usually is no. My information is partial or faulty, my thinking
half-baked. The truth about almost anything is, there is a lot to
find out and even in my own mind and emotions there's so
much going on that I can never be confident I'm aware of all of
it. So (and maybe you are like me, maybe not) I take all my
opinions with a grain of salt. Yes, these are my opinions – why
not? We all need to have opinions otherwise what would we
talk about? How could we have coffee together? How could we
commiserate and complain? But (1) these opinions aren't me
and (2) they are always subject to improvement and (3) it's not
unusual for me to hear something from someone else that gives
me a new opinion, a new idea about something. In which event
the old opinion goes, lighter than air.

And what about that biggest of big opinions? The ungraspable,
unprovable, unverifiable and, wholly unlikely, opinion that I
am a human being alive on the planet along with everyone else.
If I can appreciate the absurdity of that opinion and never forget
it, then my other opinions won't pull me down (the way you get
pulled down when you are underwater sinking fast as you hold
onto a heavy stone). Dropping the opinion is like dropping the
heavy stone, at which point you would rise automatically to the
surface.

HAYLEY FOX ROBERTS

1

"**W**HO *are you?*" was printed on the coffee cup. Good question. We're the sum of many things – our family's influences over the years, our schooling, our experiences, our fears and loves, our weaknesses and strengths as well as our creativity, dreams and purpose.

My mother named me after a hat shop – Janessa. And of such small things, these seasonings-in-the-dish-that-is-me, are our grown selves made. I hold my head high and remember that decoration, celebration and pleasure are valuable aspects of life.

The way we choose to dress or to style our hair is part of a daily self-expression. The freedom to be ourselves takes a visible form in what we pick to put on our bodies and how we show ourselves to the world. We dress for a purpose – protection, warmth, for example – but we can also dress for joy. Without following fashion for the sake of it, we can enhance the beauty of our physical form, celebrate our physical being and take pleasure in the ritual of decoration.

2

IN our dreams, so they say, we're free. We sift through our memories and daily routines; get fanciful about reality. We let our worst fears be dramatised and make them less powerful and we let our imaginations run as they please, feeding our creative thoughts. Dreams are what shape the future ... dreams in sleep and dreams in waking.

Christ was a dreamer and so was Martin Luther King. So were countless men and women who believed their world could change – that hunger could be lessened, that bigotry and intolerance could be weakened, that hope could win out over despair. Those men and women who, living their lives in oppression and distress, dream their children can be free, all make changes as they dream.

This is not magic. It's the power of belief. It's the certainty that wanting it can make it happen. From the end of apartheid in South Africa to the growth of the Pride March in Dublin, dreams of equality and civil rights move closer.

Hold onto your dreams. Dream for yourself, for those you love, for the world. And, in dreaming, believe that your dreams can come true.

3

WE'VE all spent time trying to please other people. We've tried to fit in, to be accepted. We've hoped to become what we think we're supposed to be. Often, when we're young (but not only then), we want to be part of an in-crowd. We want what others seem to have. We think being like everyone else will make us successful and happy. But that way our hopes, our desires, our needs all get lost in the strain and stretch to fit somebody else's pattern. In fear we loathe our bodies and our feelings. We want to be perfect, flawless and then, we say, everything will be all right.

But, as time passes, we can start to love ourselves with all our imperfections and weaknesses. It may take a long time to accept who we are and what we need and to know our own worth. Be patient, keep trying. Because one day when you look in the mirror the person you'll see looking through your eyes isn't some fantasy figure nor a monster – it's the self you've been hoping to meet.

And you – the combination of all your emotions, desires, struggles and loves – you've made it this far. No matter what your situation, no matter how high or low you got, you are the one truth you can rely on. Look in that mirror and recognise your self. Your individuality, your uniqueness, make you beautiful. Your space in the world is precious.

4

PICTURE a wall. Maybe you already have. Walls you built temporarily to protect yourself, to give you relief from difficult times or to hide behind. Probably when you built them they served their purpose and kept you safe, but often we forget about them when they've outlived their usefulness. The trouble with these old walls is that they stop you going anywhere.

Life is full of complications – struggles, loss, fear and grief. But being stuck and unable to move isn't much help in living through new experiences or in living life to the full either. Life is also filled with happiness, excitement and pleasure and we deserve to enjoy those feelings too. Inside those walls, we're stuck. If we could get past them we could find the strength and resources to deal with pain and fear. Beyond those walls may lie pride in our achievements, confidence in our resilience and contentment in the path we've chosen.

Picture a wall. Picture breaking it down. Beyond it, you can see the light of the future.

5

WE all feel more comfortable with 'our own kind'. When we're surrounded by people of the same colour, the same class, the same sexuality, we feel safe. We don't have to think about anyone else, only our perceived reflections of ourselves. But this world, like the richest tapestry you ever saw, is made up of millions of different threads; threads of all colours, shapes and sizes. Without that variety, life would be a bleak and passionless picture.

There's joy in the very differences between us all: the excitement of exploration and discovery; a journey to understanding a different way of life, a new culture, a new way of seeing. If we only watch reflections of similarity, gradually the world gets dulled. It loses its lustre, and monotony and unhappiness lie side by side.

Sharing differences and experiences is a way of enhancing our own lives, broadening our horizons, seeing the world as a whole and enjoying the difference. Each of our individual stitches in the story of humanity is inextricably linked. Together they can weave a tapestry that is beautiful, strong and lasts for future generations to share.

SHEENA FURLONG

1

A NYONE you meet will tell you that there is, indeed, life after the Leaving Cert. I can accept that but what I really want to know is what kind of life? And, even more importantly, will it be happy? I've asked different people what life's all about. The answers I've received have been varied and interesting but none have shone out more to me than the one of my parents. Through all adversity. My parents have been bankrupt and lived to tell the tale with a somewhat rosier ending than most of the gossips of the town would like to believe.

My dad worked hard, he still does, and will probably have to for most of his days. But, when we owned the shops in town, I never really got to see him. He'd come and kiss me goodnight most nights and we'd spend Sundays together but I never really knew the man that there was so much to know about, who had so much to tell me and so much to teach me.

When the shops closed, he was suddenly around all the time. We talked and talked. Sometimes we'd say nothing at all but I was finally coming to know the man who was caring and funny and who wanted nothing more than for me to be as happy as I could possibly be. Striving to succeed in a rapidly expanding economy that has unfortunately failed to embrace the entrepreneurial spirit that the USA cherishes, my dad has done everything in his power to please and care for his family. And for that I am eternally grateful. He has instilled in me a strength to succeed in everything that I do, and with him behind me I know I can be whoever I want to be.

2

SCHOOL as I know it is over in about 20 days time. Hopefully I'll never wear a pair of bobbly grey tights again. My A-line skirt minus the zip, button and lining will finally be put to bed. The chance of the girlie chats I've shared with my best friends every day will probably fade away too.

Those girls, Emma, Nicola, Deirdre, Amy and Laura, have gone through the mill with me. We've cried with laughter, we've panicked over exams, we've had many a screaming match and always come up smelling of roses. The thought of losing their friendship and love, good times along with all the bad times, scares me to death. And, although we'll vow to stay in touch, I can see it falling away from me already. The real likelihood is that we are going to make lots and lots of new friends and inevitably, and sadly, drift apart. Things have changed so much over the last few years and, just as I was getting used to things being the way they are, my world as I know it is being turned upside down, never to be the same again.

Very soon school trips and sleepovers will all be just a memory. The discos, the crazy clothes we used to wear, the fights and the tears will always have a special place in my heart. Along with the girls who made me who I am.

ANN HENNING JOCELYN

1

ONCE I found myself in an air emergency. Before attempting to crash land, we had to spend an hour circling to burn excess fuel. It was a very long hour. The stranger in the seat next to me held my hand and told me his whole life was passing in front of his eyes. My own mind was following a more morbid course, picturing my funeral, pondering whether there would be enough left of me to put in a coffin.

Then another thought broke through, the agonising thought my unconscious had been fighting to suppress: the toddler I had left behind, the image of him coming into our bedroom in the morning, getting into his mother's bed to start the day with a cuddle. I saw him entering this room day after day, with a bed that remained empty, where he would never again feel his mother's arms wrapped around his warm little body. It was then I realised the terrible encumbrance of parental love. How it ties us in fetters to this life, holds us to ransom, so that we can't even die gracefully without our hearts being broken. Since that day, I have only one prayer for myself – that I may live long enough to see my child able to get on without me.

2

A CONNEMARA hotelier wrote a furious letter to the county manager complaining that, in his area, renowned for outstanding natural beauty, major road repairs were consistently carried out in the height of the tourist season. *"If this wasn't sabotage,"* he growled, *"it was an example of extreme professional insensitivity."* The county engineer replied politely and regretfully, explaining that they had no option but to repair the roads in summer, as otherwise the tar wouldn't set. The hotel owner laughed when he told the story, *"Years of anger and frustration – all due to my own ignorance!"*

I was reminded of a man I knew whose childhood had been overshadowed by the fact that, aged eight, he had been dispatched to boarding school. Nobody had bothered to tell him that, in families like his, this was normal practice. He assumed he must have done something terrible to forfeit the right to his home and to his parents' love. Even after he grew up and got his facts straight, the feeling of rejection persisted. So much suffering, completely unnecessary, again due to ignorance.

It's staggering to think that, at this moment, countless lives and relationships are being ruined by virulent, destructive feelings generated by misconceptions. If only everyone ensured that they were properly informed before allowing a feeling to take root, the world wouldn't be full of fools barking up the wrong tree!

3

SO – life is a journey, a hazardous voyage of discovery; and we must negotiate our passage past adversity and trauma, undaunted, like a stream rippled by jagged rocks on its steady descent to the sea. But it's easy to lose heart, especially when we are caught in the bewildering limbo between the death of the old and the birth of the new. That's when we have to remember the phoenix who rose, time and again, from the ashes of the past. Take comfort from the knowledge that we have bypassed the greatest peril of all – that of stagnation.

The ancients looked on each crisis as a blessing, a liberation, the enforced breaking of new ground. Favourable to them was anything that helped our progress from darkness to light. There are even those who claim that extraordinary afflictions are not the punishment for extraordinary sins but the trial of extraordinary graces bestowed on a favoured few. Looking back, you may well agree that some of your worst experiences did in fact carry within them the seed of something good. Relish the shadows you leave behind. They add depth and definition. For expansion, though, look forward: into the dazzling new dimension of the unknown. You'll see that there are no endings in life. Only beginnings.

4

MY only child has just started boarding school. The house is painfully empty. It was the boy himself who wanted to go, backed up by his father. I resisted, with rational arguments and less rational emotions. In the end I confronted my husband and asked him why he wanted to send our son away to school. *"Because I believe he would benefit"* was his straight answer.

In the sleepless night that followed, I had to admit he was right. By daybreak I had accepted that, whatever my own feelings, I had no right to hold up a process that would assist my child in his social and academic development. And I remembered the lines my mother wrote in a notebook the day I left home to study in a foreign country:

> *When you were born, I said to myself, "I shall never again be alone."*

> *Little did I realise that the infant I cradled in my arms was given to me on loan, to care for and prepare for the day when I would hand her over to another life that I can share only from a distance.*

5

MY mother, aged 70, was in a horrific motor accident. For days she was on life support; both her legs had to be amputated. *"The poor woman,"* said my well-meaning neighbour, *"wouldn't it be better if she was just left to die?"*

Before her last operation, she was able to talk to me.

"I don't know what I'm fighting for," she said. *"What sort of life do I have to look forward to, even if I do survive?"*

"That's for you to decide," I answered. *"Only you can tell whether life in a wheelchair would still be worth living."*

She thought about this for a while, and then she stated, *"What I value most is having my children; follow you as you grow older; see how your lives develop. Be there for you when you need me."*

She survived. She recovered. Today, nine years later, she lives alone in an adapted flat where her daily routine is much the same as usual, except, amazingly, she's happier than before; enjoying a late blossoming. With a brand-new interest to sustain her, she depends on no one; her life is her own. But now and then she remembers that critical moment, when a mother's love for her children made all the difference.

RITA ANN HIGGINS

1

DURING my residency in Tullamore, I stayed in a very posh bed and breakfast. Once I forgot to book for the following week and I had to find alternative accommodation. This other place had no telly in the room, no en-suite, no tea- or coffee-making facilities. I didn't sleep well either. I woke up at about five in the morning and started to read the novel *Cold Mountain* by Charles Fraser. The next morning I slept it out. The woman of the house woke me with her gentle tapping on the bedroom door. *"Get up, love,"* she said, *"your breakfast is ready. I have to go to 10 o'clock mass. Your breakfast is on the table. I try to go every day for Lent,"* she said. *"Will you get up out of it?"* Something about the tone of her voice or the familiar way she said *"your breakfast is on the table"* made me feel very secure. The breakfast was big and delicious. I was embarrassed to tell her that I had broken the blind in my room by pulling it down too far. *"Don't worry about the blind, love,"* she said. *"It will be there long after us."*

2

ONE day when I was coming back from Tullamore, I met Louise on the train. She told me about her time in Austria. Her friend got a job minding children there. She had a lovely family; they brought her on holiday with them. Her room was cosy, it had every possible comfort. She was allowed to use the phone if she needed to ring home. Louise couldn't wait to be a childminder in Austria. Unfortunately *Ní mar a shíltear a bítear* (things are never as they seem). Louise knew the moment she met the woman at the airport that things were not going to work out. *"I knew by the way she looked at me,"* says Louise. The house was beautiful. It was three hours from the airport. It was out in the middle of nowhere. Louise never got to mind the children. They left the house early in the morning with the parents and they didn't return until about five every evening. Louise was in the house all day on her own, cleaning and ironing.

After about two weeks she told the woman of the house that she wanted to go home to Ireland. The woman said her husband would be furious. Louise was sick with nerves. The husband did drive her to the airport, but he never spoke all the way except when he pulled in for petrol. He said a few really angry things but not in English. She told me the night before she left she kept her passport under her pillow just in case. In the short time she was there, she never heard anyone laugh. Not even the children.

3

THE day I finished my residency in Tullamore, I was heading back to Galway. I met a young woman on the train and we got talking. She told me she was a pastry chef in Tullamore. We started to talk about food in general and nice places we had eaten in. I told her about a restaurant we had come across in Moycullen. She told me a lot about her favourite foods and the places she liked to eat. She gave every detail. We both made a point of saying we didn't eat out often.

After lots more food talk, I told her I couldn't eat anything with flour in it, as it didn't agree with me. She told me she had two easy dessert recipes that didn't require flour and that if I liked she would call them out to me. I got out my notebook. She called out what ingredients I needed for chocolate roulade and meringue roulade. I wrote everything down like an obedient child full of wonder. She said the only thing was, if I didn't already have one, I would need to get a Swiss roll tray. I told her I'd buy one specially. Soon enough we were pulling into Ceannt Station in Galway. *"Giorraíonn beirt bóthair"* (two shorten the road). We parted as if we were old friends. I left the train two recipes heavier.

4

THE day before my husband was due back from London after visiting with our eldest daughter, I thought I would invite two of my friends up for lunch. We had an unhurried lunch. My friends brought up wine and strawberries and cream. It didn't go astray. The house was tidier than usual that day. We had a great time talking and laughing. I was showing off the garden and the new sliding door we'd put in some months earlier, greedy for extra light. That day I was reminded of an old Irish proverb, "*Is fearr cáirde ná ór*" (friends are better than gold). Afterwards we went for a walk on a nearby beach. A beach I try to visit every day for a quiet walk to keep me on the straight and narrow. A place without MTV or the *Six o'clock News*. We walked for about an hour, the three of us. As we were walking and talking, I thought to myself, *"I've known these women for 20 years and I don't believe I have a photograph of the three of us together."* When they left at about half five I told my daughter about the lovely walk we'd had and how I thought about the fact that we didn't have a photograph of the three of us. My Leaving-Certer said that sometimes you didn't need photographs.

5

MY mother and father are dead now. One time I asked my father for some cuttings from my mother's peony rose. *"The time isn't right yet,"* he said. Months later he turned up with some tubers in a plastic bag. That was the first and last time he was in my house. He planted them in our front garden, in the corner where they had room to flourish. They did flourish every year. But people always plucked the buds from the roses that flopped just outside the wall. My husband, with the green fingers, moved my mother's peony rose into the back garden. I enjoy it now from the kitchen window until its own weight brings it forward and the petals fall.

My mother used to get petals from the peony rose blessed and give them to her friends. They would keep them in their wallets or in the corner of a purse. The petals were blessed on the feast of St Rita, sometime in May. One day I met a woman who told me my mother had given her a petal from a peony rose 35 years ago. She said she would like me to have that petal. I keep it at the back of my passport.

ROSE MARY LOGUE

1

STORIES are told in the Sufi tradition about Sheik Nasrudin, a lovable but foolish man with foibles that would not be out of character with your typical Irish man or woman. Once, while travelling in India, he came to a fruit and vegetable market and noticed that many people were buying chillies. He hadn't encountered them before and thought that, if they were so popular, he would treat himself to some. He bought two kilos, found a shady spot for his lunch and started to eat. He chewed the first chilli and was instantly moaning and fanning his mouth to try to relieve the heat. He optimistically picked out another, thinking that it would taste better. He went on, working his way through his two kilos of chillies, and was soon foaming at the mouth.

A man who had been watching walked up to Nasrudin and asked him what he was doing. *"Look,"* he said, *"these are chillies – they are only to be eaten in very small quantities."* Nasrudin kept eating. The man was amazed that, now that he knew what chillies were, he wouldn't stop eating them. *"Well,"* said Nasrudin, *"I bought these chillies with good money and I'm going to eat them, no matter what."*

We're all like that sometimes. What we do does not satisfy us, but we continue on the same path, each day thinking that what has failed before must succeed today.

2

ONCE during the course of his travels, Sheik Nasrudin met a yogi and a priest. Soon they were talking about God and what they did for Him, what sacrifices they made in their lives for His sake. The yogi drew a circle on the ground and said, *"Everything I get I throw in the air. What falls inside the circle is for God and what falls outside the circle is for me."* The priest drew a similar circle and said, *"Everything I get I throw in the air. What falls outside the circle is for God and what falls inside the circle is for me."* Nasrudin was not to be outdone in stating his generosity. He said, *"I don't bother drawing a circle. Everything I get I throw into the air. I say, 'Dear God, I offer you my wealth: accept whatever portion you want.' He keeps what He needs and everything that falls to the ground is for me."*

We're a lot like this at times. We like to think we are doing great things for God but can delude ourselves. While we make our decisions to suit ourselves, we can persuade ourselves that we are doing all from a higher motive.

3

NASRUDIN was keen to go out into the world to find God, although his father wanted him to stay at home and help look after the shrine of which he was custodian. However, the father gave Nasrudin a donkey and he spent many years wandering to and fro. Finally, one day, the donkey collapsed and died by the side of the road. Nasrudin sat down beside the body and cried bitterly. Passers-by saw his distress and sympathised by placing leaves and branches over the body; others covered it with clay; some brought flowers to lay on the mound. When others saw the mound covered in flowers, they assumed it was the burial mound of a great being and left money and other offerings. Priests, incense sellers and florists arrived. Soon a huge mosque was built and as more and more people came it became very wealthy. When Nasrudin's father heard of the fame of the mosque he came on a visit and was amazed to find the custodian was his long-lost son. Nasrudin was overjoyed as he could at last tell somebody what was troubling him.

"Father, this is the shrine of the donkey you gave me."

"That's strange," said his father, *"that's exactly how my shrine came into being – it also started with a donkey."*

That is how empty worship is, without realisation that the Kingdom of God is within.

4

SHEIK Nasrudin went out one night and got very drunk with his friends. He staggered down the road and fumbled with his key trying to get into his house. After some time, fruitless effort, much cursing and complaining, the window above the door opened and his wife poked her head out.

"Who is it?" she enquired.

"It's me," said Nasrudin, *"come down and let me in."*

The wife wasn't inclined to come down on such a cold night and said, *"Why are you wandering around out there? Have you lost your key? Let yourself in!"*

"I have the key," Nasrudin said, *"the problem is that the door has no lock."*

We're a bit like Nasrudin sometimes, searching for God and not finding Him, unable, because of our blindness and drunkenness, to find Him where He has always been. But He is there, closer than we ever could imagine. He is there in the small, precious things of life: family and community, joy and sorrow, summer and winter. He is deep in our hearts, leading us in our perplexity, nurturing us in our hunger, soothing us in our distress. The Kingdom of God is among us.

5

SHEIK Nasrudin woke up one morning before even the first light of dawn – it was still pitch black. He called out and woke his disciple and said,

"Go outside, Mahmud, and see if the sun is up yet."

Mahmud went outside and was soon back. *"It's pitch black out there,"* he said. *"There is no sign of the sun."*

At this Nasrudin became very angry. *"You fool!"* He shouted. *"Haven't you got the sense to use a flashlight!"*

Swami Muktananda advises that to expect a spiritual technique to reveal the indwelling God is like expecting a flashlight to illuminate the sun. He says we must meditate and perform spiritual practices in order to make the intellect pure enough to reflect the light of God. He tells us:

> *"Sit very quietly in your chair, then turn within and try to see who watches your thoughts from inside. If you keep watching in that way, you will come to know the Self, who is a God. You are looking for what you have never lost. So turn within. Look for that inner knower. God is in your heart. You lost Him in your heart. You will only find Him in your heart."*

RICHARD MARSH

1

THIS is a traditional Japanese Buddhist story with Christian overtones.

There was a woman who was notorious for her meanness. She was born selfish, lived all her life selfishly, and died selfish. Years later, when her son died and went to heaven, he discovered to his surprise that his mother was not there. She had been sent to hell for her meanness. The son asked Buddha to please move his mother to heaven. Buddha said that might be possible, but only if it could be proved that she had performed at least one act of generosity during her life on earth. The son was allowed to look at the celestial records of his mother's life, but after a thorough investigation he was able to find only one instance in which she had given something to someone. A beggar had come to the house looking for food, and she had given him a leek.

The laws of time and space were suspended while a search was carried out for that particular leek at that precise time. The leek was found and handed over to Buddha. Buddha reached the lower end of the leek into hell and told the woman to hold onto it while he held the upper end. The woman did so, and Buddha began to draw her up out of hell. But before she reached heaven, the leek broke under her weight and she fell back into hell, where she stayed.

The leek broke because it was rotten, which was the only reason the woman had given it to the beggar.

2

YESTERDAY I told you about the mean woman who gave a rotten leek to a beggar. Here is the opposite side of the coin. This story is set in the 1940s or 1950s and is popular among American storytellers. My source for it is in the form of a first-person narrative by a nurse who claimed to be present. The story may seem improbable and overly sentimental to some, but I defy anyone to scoff.

A little girl was suffering from a serious but unspecified disease. Her five-year-old brother had also contracted the disease, but he had recovered. The girl's only chance for survival was to receive a transfusion and, since her brother's blood contained the antibodies needed to fight the disease, he was the ideal donor. The doctor explained the situation to the boy in what he thought were terms appropriate to the comprehension level of a five-year-old. He told him that his sister would die unless he donated blood to her, and he asked him if he was willing to do that. The boy took a deep breath and without hesitation said, *"Yes, if that's the only thing that will save her."* Since the boy asked no questions, the doctor assumed – mistakenly – that he understood exactly what was involved.

The procedure got underway immediately. It was a direct transfusion, with the brother and sister lying side by side on the bed. The boy watched his blood flow into his sister's body, and he smiled when he saw a healthy pink glow return to her cheeks. Then his smile faded, and he looked up at the doctor and asked with a quiver in his voice, *"Will I start to die right away?"*

3

THIS is a Chinese variant of an international tale.

Ming Lo and his wife lived next door to a large mountain. In winter, the cold from the snow on top of the mountain seeped into their bones. In summer, the mountain blocked cool breezes from the sea, so that they sweltered in the heat. And any time of the year, rocks bounced down the side of the mountain and made holes in the roof of their house.

They decided to get rid of the mountain, but they didn't know how to go about it. So they went to a wise man, explained the problem and asked his advice. The wise man told them to cut down a tree and use it to push the mountain out of the way. They tried that, but it didn't work. The wise man then suggested bribing the mountain to go away by giving it sweet cakes. *That* didn't work. They tried banging pots and pans to frighten the mountain into leaving but that didn't work either. Finally, the wise man said, *"You'll have to use the mountain-moving dance. That never fails."* And he taught them how to do the dance. *"Take your house apart and bundle it up with your belongings and put everything on top of your heads. Next, you face the mountain and close your eyes. Then you place your left foot behind your right foot, then your right foot behind your left foot, and continue to do that for one whole day. Then open your eyes, and you will see that the mountain has moved."* Ming Lo and his wife did the dance exactly as the wise man instructed and, when they opened their eyes, they were delighted to find that the mountain had indeed moved.

4

THIS African tale is a favourite with storytellers who work with young people in drug-prevention programmes, although it is certainly not limited to that application.

Bowane the Civet Cat met a beautiful female Civet Cat in another village and asked her to marry him, and she said, *"Yes."* So Bowane went back to his own village to gather presents and get dressed in his finest clothes and invite his friends to the wedding. He set off for the wedding with his friends Embenga the Pigeon flapping beside him, Nguma the Python slithering along on the other side, and Ulu the Tortoise waddling behind the other three.

They had not gone far when Embenga the Pigeon found he was so hungry he couldn't go on. He asked Bowane to wait until some palm nuts ripened so that he could eat them, and Bowane waited. Before they were half-way to the village, Nguma the Python caught an antelope and ate it. He asked Bowane to wait until he digested it, and Bowane waited. And then they came to a log across the path. Ulu the Tortoise asked Bowane to wait until it rotted, because he couldn't climb over it, and Bowane waited.

By the time they reached the village of Bowane's intended bride, they found that she had got married and already had two children. Bowane was very upset. He explained why he was so late and he accused her of being unfaithful to him. This made her angry, and she said, *"Did you think you could keep me waiting forever? Did you never consider saying 'No' to your friends?"*

5

PERHAPS the major criticism older people have of the younger generation is that they seem to have no ideals, no plans to change the world for the better. They don't think it's possible for one person to make a difference, and, even if it *is* possible, they're too self-centred to bother. Loren Eiseley told this story in his 1964 book *The Unexpected Universe*. It's not clear whether he made it up or was transmitting a traditional tale.

A young man was walking along a beach when he saw in the distance an old man picking things up from the sand and throwing them into the sea. As he came closer, he could see that the things were starfish that had been stranded on the beach. He asked the man why he was throwing the starfish into the water.

"These starfish will die if they're left here on the beach," said the man, *"and I come out here every day and throw as many back into the sea as I can."*

"But there are hundreds of starfish on this beach," the young man said. *"And there must be millions on beaches around the world. What difference does it make if you throw a few of them back into the sea?"*

The old man picked up another starfish and said, *"It makes a lot of difference to this one,"* and threw it back into the water.

The obvious moral to the story is that *one* person *can* make a difference, but perhaps a moral more applicable to today's self-centred youth is this: you *can* change the world, if only a little bit at a time, but you have to do it quickly, before the world changes *you*.

GERALDINE MILLS

1

I HAD been watching the holly berries turn since early autumn. Green for so long, then a slow development of spectrum. Each day they seemed to get brighter and brighter until one morning there was a fire of red burning on the trees around our home.

We gathered these flames of colour and brought armfuls to brighten the dullest corners, grace the tops of cupboards, get the house ready for Christmas. But now with the decorations returned to the attic, the dried-up brittle holly used for kindling, the house was resigned to being its colourless self.

We took a walk in the woods, my son and I, and came across a treasure, a holly tree still carrying its berries. Despite all other trees having been shaven clean, for some unknown reason neither birds nor humans had laid eyes on this one.

I asked my young son to help me break off the branches so that I could return some winter colour to the house we just left. He was indignant. How could I deny the birds their winter food just so that we could decorate the house? I told him that they were my food in this season of dark days. He was not convinced.

We negotiated, he on behalf of the birds, I on behalf of me. After some time we settled on a compromise. I would take two small branches, just two so that I could hold onto this flame of colour that would bring me through the dark crucible of winter skies. All the rest would be left for the pigeons and the thrushes to feast as they wished when they found them.

2

THERE is a cobweb on each of the six panes of my front door. The weak morning sun shines through them and brings them into sharp focus as I work my way down the hall. Six cobwebs in various stages of completeness. Some are no more than foundation lines, others are complete except for the centre. These show signs of a struggle, pieces of wing, skeletons of prey tied to silk. Unsuspecting wingers that flew too close and never got back to tell the tale. The last cobweb on the lowest right corner is however intact; a complete work of art and engineering. My eye picks out lines parallel, equidistant, the central hub perfect. I see the spider hiding behind one of the wooden dividers. He looks like he is asleep, his legs all curled up underneath him. He has built himself a brand new snare; waiting, listening, through his world wide web, for some interloper to fly this way. He knows by the vibrations on the web if he has breakfast.

I check all my other windows. They are the same. Cobwebs stretch from corner to corner. Threads of silk wrap up our house like a cocoon. Callers must look at the house, think it is like something from a B-rated horror movie and scurry away frightened.

Someday, maybe in spring when the energy is rising, I will rush out with my bucket and mop and put paid to all their hard work in my madness to spring-clean. But, right now, I would be a vandal to destroy them.

3

'UNU la ta nee' or 'the Cold Month' was the name the Native Americans gave to January. And they were right. Trees skinned to the bone. A meanness of wind that grips me as I turn a corner unsuspecting. The constant threat of freezing. Skies so low it feels like they are pushing me into the ground. I am left standing in this new year as if on a pier burdened by all this baggage that I have brought with me, and the knowledge that the vessel that has carried me thus far has already turned and pulled out to sea.

Last year's journey was turbulent enough but I had come to gauge the swell, that sudden unprepared-for surge. I am half-way through this cold month, not knowing what sort of sea monsters this ocean of new year will throw up.

My spirit needs reassurance that it is made of such stuff to tackle these creatures of the deep. I search my day for some glimpse to set me on the right course. If I bow to the earth I see bulbs that I planted in another season begin to cut through the earth like knife blades. There is a 'hen's kick' in the length of the day. I look up at the cup of stars spilling over into the night sky.

In the months ahead, a whole new uncharted map waits for me to explore. Learning from last year's lessons to use my compass better, I look forward, forever hoping to find where true north lies.

4

WHILE commuters face the headache of morning rush hour, I have taken myself to a place where traffic is not an issue, on this scrap of road between the blue windows of my cottage and the wild waves of the Kerry Atlantic. I have come to write in the Cill Rialaig Project in Baile an Sceilig. All I have with me are the tools of my trade: my notebooks, my pen and ink. I take a morning step upon the road. The sun is coming up over Scariff Island. It lays a silver path across the sea so convincingly that I could walk to Waterville in its shimmer. This morning I am free of worry about the car starting in dampness, tailbacks on the Headford Road roundabout. It is so quiet I can hear my heart beat as I climb the hill. I can hear my head speak of wondrous things, my eyes speak of wondrous sights, of stones that stand up to history, of birds that hang in the air, weightless. I can hear the day. The only thing that is in a hurry is the stream that gathers somewhere up on the mountain, weaves its way down past the restrictions of rock, overtakes me and rushes headlong into the sea. I turn, look back at the village so well set into the hill, almost indecipherable in the letter and line of morning shadow. The only traffic restriction I meet is a sheep in the grass centre of the road. He stares at me. He could bleat that this walkway is his, yet he veers to the side, runs down among the rocks, and the road is all mine.

Let me bring this moment with me when I return to the world of cars, that I may remember gentle road etiquette; that I too may be generous and give way.

5

THIS is early morning light. I sit at my table recording those first thoughts that spring from the chink of knowing between sleep and wake. The sky is a brooding indigo, augury of the shower so big coming across the hills that will deluge us in no time. The wind begins to rise and I watch the shower as it moves in to attack. It hounds the panes of our curtainless windows. It beats off the glass as if trying to get in, so loud its heavy thud is bound to wake my sleeping family as it rages overhead. I look out to the left and right and in front of me. There are strings of water beads falling to earth, on the long grass where the wind rushes the wintering of things. My cat comes running down the field, a tortoiseshell roll in a field of dying grass, finds the one cloche with an easy access and hides there from the demon overhead. The wind battles the branches of the rowans, the dried out umbels of angelica. My son's look-out tower takes the greatest beating; its camouflage becomes birds of moss and leaves that are blown across the morning air. It has collapsed by the time the clouds shift to pour down over the stone fort on the hill.

All signs indicate we are in for a bad day; but then, like many things in life when we confront the worst and accept it, we can be surprised by a whisper of change. The sky slowly begins to lighten from its indigo to something resembling blue and the storm clouds move off into the other villages and away over the Corrib to beat upon the islands of the lake. As the sky brightens, the house begins to purr like a giant cat being stroked by the hand of God. I have written the storm out.

SEÁN MONCRIEFF

1

IF the span of a life follows any sort of pattern, it is this. Once you've achieved adulthood, you knock about the place for a while. You attend a lot of 21st birthday parties. Some time after this, you find that you are going to an awful lot of weddings. One of them may even be your own. A few years later, you find that the weddings circuit appears to have dried up, but now there are a fierce amount of christenings to attend. You may have an involvement in these also.

The situation remains fairly static for some years after this, everyone being busy with the kids and all. But, eventually, it's time to start attending 40th birthday parties. I went to my first one a few weeks back. Not my own, I hasten to add. It was attended mostly by people I've known for years, people I've met at 21sts and weddings and christenings, everyone a little bit tubbier or balder or greyer – or all three. Everyone a little bit startled that someone they know had actually got to be 40 years of age. And sooner or later, *they* would too.

Oh, I know all these things are relative: if you're 20, turning 21 seems the end of the world; once you're 30, you might as well start shopping for coffins. It's not the same though – to be 40 is to be undeniably middle-aged. At the party, virtually everyone I met made a reference to this, though not for very long. It seemed to be forgotten about in the first hour. We stayed there until the wee small hours, then went to a nightclub full of 20-year-olds. OK, we only stayed five minutes, but it's the principle of the thing that counts.

2

IF you live in a city, and especially Dublin, here's something you can try the next time you go into the city centre. From the moment you've got off the bus or parked your car, glance at your watch: time how long it takes before someone asks you for money. I've taken to doing this recently whenever I go into the centre of Dublin. So far, my record is 15 seconds. It's never been longer than three minutes.

I started timing it because I had established a rule for myself whenever I went into town: I would give money to the first person who asked, thus allowing myself to refuse everyone else. I felt I needed to do this because the bombardment of requests had become oppressive: I needed a strategy to negotiate past my own guilt and irritation.

I am not, I think, untypical in this. I can't think of anyone I know who isn't uncomfortable at having to step over 12-year-olds living in cardboard boxes. Yet it's precisely this reaction which should be far more unsettling. When we go into Habitat to buy our trendy lamps, we don't want to be faced with poverty and squalor on our way there. So we devise rules and strategies to deal with this, to make ourselves feel better. Not them. If the poor disappeared off the streets tomorrow, most of us probably wouldn't even wonder where they had gone. What the hell is wrong with us?

3

WHAT are men going to do? What do men do now?

They wear shirts and ties and go out to work and act all tough
and responsible. They go to the pub and drink pints and talk
about football. Only about football. Men don't talk about their
feelings or any of that woosie stuff. Let's face it, men barely
have feelings, certainly none of any intensity. You don't see
men bursting into tears. No one wants to see men bursting into
tears.

Then again, times have changed. Men oppressed women for
centuries and should, rightly, be sorry for this. They have to
learn to accommodate women into the world as equals, they
should do their fair share around the house, they should even
learn to become a bit more sensitive. But not too sensitive, mind,
because no one likes a wimp. Men still have to be manly, they
still have to act like they are strong enough to handle any situation. Woe betide the man that says, *"Oh, it's all a bit too much for
me. I'd like some help."* No one is interested in men like that.
What we want are men who are tough and silent, yet who can
also be vulnerable and talk a lot. Alright, yes, that's a contradiction. So let's think of an example of this. A well-known, male
role-model . . . eerrm. OK, I can't think of one. But there must be
one. Men like that do exist. They must.

What are men going to do?

4

IF you've got kids, you may well have experienced this. I've just experienced it now, as I write the script I'm reading to you. It's probably the last sunny weekend of the diminishing summer and all the family are in the back garden. The parents plan to relax, foolishly hoping that the kids can entertain themselves. The garden is crowded with toys, yet it seems as if their entertainment value is limited – before long the eight-year-old is amusing himself by holding a dolly hostage. The owner of the dolly, his two-year-old sister, screams with an ear-piercing, theatrical despair. The parents scream now, until the dolly is released.

But the peace is short lived – within minutes a teddy bear has been abducted and the wails of anguish begin again. More shouting from the parents. The teddy is eventually returned, the eight-year-old chastened. This avenue of fun now cut off, he mopes around for a while, then approaches his parents and utters the most annoying phrase any child can come up with.

"I'm bored."

"Read a book then."

"No. That's boring. What'll I do? I'm so bored.*"* I have to write scripts, so their mother brings them off to a friend's house. Peace descends on our home. Yet now I can't concentrate. The silence is almost eerie. I look at his muddy bicycle, at her row of dollies lined up in their miniature pushchairs. And I wonder how long it will be before they are back.

5

SINCE I've been 18 years of age or so, I've carried around this vague notion that I wanted to be a writer. I don't exactly know why. I've always loved books and I suppose I was infected with the idea that writers know more than ordinary mortals. They sit in their ivy-covered houses and think deep thoughts. If you're going to be a writer, you have to have an ivy-covered house.

But, as I say, it was a vague notion, and while I could talk and walk like a writer, and often checked the property pages for ivy-covered premises, I didn't actually do much writing. Eventually, even I noticed this contradiction and was forced to put up or shut up. I bought a huge second-hand desk and set about writing my novel. I bought a fat Cuban cigar which I would smoke on the day I received that breathless phone call from a grateful publisher. I don't know much about cigars, but I doubt if they get better with age, certainly not if they have been lying in a dusty drawer for over 10 years. Several unpublished books later, it is still there.

Real life has gone on. Marriage, kids, job, a house free of ivy. I have realised that, in all these areas, there is little to complain about. I have realised too that, despite being unpublished, I enjoy writing my books – it is worth doing for its own sake. It was enough. Until four months ago, when I received a phone call from a London publisher telling me that he loved a manuscript I had sent him. That he wanted to print it and stick it in the shops. It's coming out next year. I didn't smoke my cigar. Instead I chain-smoked five cigarettes and wondered was someone playing a cruel joke on me. A dream come true can be a scary thing.

RABBI JULIA NEUBERGER

1

THE *Ethics of the Fathers* is a collection of teachings from the Mishnah, a Jewish codification of the law dating to around AD200. Much of the teaching is not very different from that of Jesus, who would have been a contemporary of some of the rabbis quoted. Some of the strands of Jesus' equivocal attitude to authority – at best – and his view about the worth of the ordinary person can be found in *The Ethics of the Fathers*. Here's an example: Shemaiah said, *"Love labour, and hate mastery, and don't seek the acquaintance of the ruling power."* In other words, treat the occupying power – in this case the Romans – with care, and don't suck up to them.

And Rabban Gamliel said, *"Be heedful of the ruling power, for they bring no person near them except for their own need; they seem to be friends when it is in their interest, but they don't stick with you when the things get bad."*

So what has changed? We see ourselves as needing 'political skills'. We think we must lobby, must make friends with those who hold power. And yet, how many of those people will come to our help when things get rough? Both Jewish and Christian literature, with all their realism about human nature, could see how 'political brown-nosing', as the Americans put it, is dangerous. And, in both our literatures, we hear a cry for different values: helping the honest person, and loving the ordinary, as much as, if not more than, the great and the good. At a time of political scandals, and a time when many of the young are saying 'a plague on all your houses' about the political process, it's worth remembering that some of this has been said for 2,000 years or so.

2

A NOTHER of the sayings from *The Ethics of the Fathers* concerns women, and it drives me crazy. It always seems to me to make it clear how very male those groups who discussed the law were in ancient days – and often still are. And it always makes me feel we need some women in there writing 'Ethics of the Mothers'. Here's an example:

"Let your house be wide open, and let all the needy come to you and be part of your household... " Fine thus far – you couldn't object – but then it continues, *"and talk not much with womankind"*. They said this of a man's own wife. How much the more so of the wife of his neighbour. Hence the sages say, *"He that talks with womankind brings evil upon himself, neglects the study of the law, and will at the end inherit Gehenna"* (that is, go to hell).

Nasty stuff, this, and worth emphasising for its very nastiness. It makes it abundantly clear that whoever wrote this was a woman hater, and it makes women who are religious, or interested in religion, all the more determined to look for other interpretations and new insights that recognise women's spirituality. There are wonderful things to be found in our Jewish teachings, but this particular section isn't one of them, and we have to be brave enough, in all our traditions, to say when we think our ancestors got it wrong.

3

ONE of the oldest teachings in *The Ethics of the Fathers* comes from Simeon the Just, who was either the son of Onias the High Priest around 280 BC or High Priest himself around 200 BC. He used to say, *"By three things the world is sustained, by the law, by worship, and by deeds of loving kindness."* The law was not the law as we now understand it, but the Torah, God's law as they saw it, which it was a duty to study and obey. Worship was also different, for this was still in Temple times, and probably meant formal Temple services and rituals we might not approve of now. But the interesting one is 'deeds of loving kindness'. For what are they?

Well, every Jew is commanded to give *tsedakah*, what we call charity but is nearer to meaning a donation in order to even things up a bit. And that's a minimum of 10 percent of one's income, and is the origin of the *tithe*. But if one gives a lot more, out of the goodness of one's heart rather than as a religious duty, which is all the first lot is, then it's deeds of loving kindness. It's over 20 percent of one's income. It's going over the top. It's doing things that are horrible in order to alleviate another person's suffering. Simeon didn't believe the world depended just on the giving of ordinary charity, the evening up of things, as one might put it. For him there needed to be a real effort, something out of the ordinary, something that showed real devotion to fellow human beings. That's what's meant by deeds of loving kindness, and it is those deeds, most of us feel even now, that make the world a better place. It's going beyond the ordinary, and it's doing something out of love for other human beings, including those we do not know.

4

HILLEL was one of the most famous of the rabbis. He lived around 30 BC to about AD10, and was author of one of the most often quoted of the sayings from *The Ethics of the Fathers*. It goes like this: *"If I am not for myself, who is for me? If I'm only for myself, what am I? And if not now, when?"* People have discussed exactly what he meant, but it's something like this.

If I don't stand up for myself, no one will – a certain level of esteem is essential, and perhaps the meekness and humility that we sometimes see amongst apparently religious people isn't what we should encourage.

But if I only stand up for myself, and not for others, I'm no kind of human being at all – the role of the good person must be to take on the cause of the weak, the needy, the oppressed. All perfectly obvious, good stuff.

The hardest bit is the one I think matters most. If not now, when? You can't put it off. If I say I'll do it tomorrow, I am not being true to myself or to my tradition. If there is someone needy, if there is action I ought to take on behalf of someone else, then I ought to do it *now*. Procrastination isn't acceptable. This is the time to carry out what I know I should.

That sense of urgency is very marked in much of these teachings. But Hillel, one of the earliest and the greatest of these teachers, makes it very clear. If you don't do it now, when will you do it? And don't tell me tomorrow, or next week, because that simply will not do. Go out and do good now.

5

MY last in this series from *The Ethics of the Fathers* is my favourite of them all. It isn't very different in kind from some of the others, but it's so beautifully put. It goes like this: *"The day is short and the task is great. The labourers are idle and the wage is abundant and the master of the house is pressing."* You don't have very long in this world, and there is much to do. The rewards are plenty, but we human beings are idle creatures who do not get on with it, and the master of the house, God, is in a hurry and wants to see us do the right thing and try and create a decent world here on earth. It continues, *"It is not your duty to finish the work, but you are not free to stop doing it either."* No one is expected to do the impossible, but you cannot say that, because the task is so enormous, because there is so much to do for our fellow human beings, we shouldn't even begin. We have to get in there and do it.

I love the sense of urgency that is conveyed by Rabbi Tarfon's saying. God is in a hurry, and we, His people, cannot hang about. We can't do it all, but we can't hide from our obligation either. Whether that's giving charity, going to help, doing kindly deeds for a neighbour, or whatever, God's in a hurry and wants to see us in there. I believe that we have lost that sense of urgency in many of our world religions. We spend time fighting over faith, or explaining it. We talk of the duties of religion, and what it does and doesn't allow. It's about what you can eat, who you can sleep with, whether there is divorce, what women can do. And I mind about all of these things. But in the end it comes down to this: there's a lot of suffering out there, and we human beings are quite capable of alleviating it, as well as being good at causing it. Our God-given duty is to get out there and do what we can. Though Rabbi Tarfon was a Jew, that's a view that could go for all of us, whatever our faith. And that sense of urgency is one we should carry with us in our hearts, every day.

EIBHLÍN NIC EOCHAIDH

1

THE red suitcase stands beside the wardrobe door accusingly. It has stood there since I carried it in from the boot of the car three weeks ago. It is full of clothes that hung in a wardrobe in Dublin while I lived there for a year, Mondays to Fridays.

Now the year is over. I am home again in Leitrim away from the alarm-call of early-morning commuter traffic outside my window on Lower Kimmage Road; away from mobile phones ringing continuously on buses, voices speaking languages I do not understand; away from the impatient surge of people trying to cross the road at the junction of Nassau Street and Dawson Street.

It is hard to let go, to move on. Returning from holidays I fill the bottom of that suitcase with pieces of bark, seeds and pods, assorted shells, the leaf of an almond tree – trying to carry something of one place with me into another. Now the bits and pieces sit on a window ledge and gather dust.

The sun shines through the window, highlighting a spider's web in the top left-hand corner. Strongly anchored, the threads barely move in the draught. A spider starts to climb the wall. Delicately bending and extending a feeler, she tests her way forward.

Maybe moving on is like that? A matter of dogged persistence, a case of putting one foot in front of the other, step after step after step.

2

I MADE a list of all the things I'll miss about Dublin. The list includes streetwise pigeons, workers, tourists, students, all dicing with death under the wheels of cars at College Green; the monument to Oscar Wilde in Merrion Square and the night-time window of Mad Flowers on Dame Street – a still life as arresting as any in our National Gallery.

But what I'll miss most is the 'hardness' of the city – the feel of pavement underfoot; the continual sense of being confronted by the vertical hardness of walls, houses, shops; the surprise of lifting my eyes from the horizontal line of city streets to a space occupied by cranes moving in a *t'ai chi* routine across the city's skyline. The possibility of turning corners into surprise; adventure and discovery seems more alive in the landscape of the city. There are less corners here in Leitrim. The landscape unfolds, enfolds around me. At the bottom of the garden, across two fields, the mountain rises to spread itself across the available horizon.

The first night home from Dublin, I went out to close the gate at bedtime. Rounding the gable of the house, I found myself looking, for a startled moment, straight into the eyes of a young fox caught in the glare of the outside light. We stood staring at each other until he ran back into the night.

Today I thought of the last lines of a poem by Holly Spaulding:

> *I want so much that is not here*
> *and yet*
> *is this enough?*

3

LOOKING for something else in a stack of books, magazines and folders, I come across a sheet of paper with a sentence scribbled on it in pencil. It is my own handwriting, my own words. *"I am lost in middle age, with no map to guide me, how to move forward or go back."*

I love maps. All those maps of Ireland we drew in National School, tracing from the atlas through greaseproof paper, transferring them carefully into our copies, then painstakingly colouring them in – the blue squiggly rivers, the brown miniature mountain ranges. Or the maps in fairy-tale books – the empty desert expanse that was marked, 'Here be Dragons'. Or the map of the river in *Tarka, the Otter* – the landscape I had created in my mind made visible in black-and-white drawing. When we moved to Leitrim, we bought a large-scale ordnance survey map of the surrounding area. Our house didn't exist on the map. A stone over what used to be the front door reads 1933. Later we found out the house had been re-roofed and plastered that year. On the hill below us was marked a well, with a broken line indicating a path across the field. We went looking for the well, searching for days. Jim, our neighbour, told us that it had closed in, disappeared. No trace remained of the well-used path either. The house it led to on the map was empty. It's thatched roof fallen in, a home now for cattle. Near the upper road there was a well, still in daily use and regularly maintained. Not long after, it dried up. The water that had flowed for years diverted, disappeared.

Middle age can feel like that sometimes – a dried up well, a barren desert – 'Here be Dragons'. I search for the clues, messages left by other travellers to guide me on my way. I find one in a book by Starhawk. She speaks of middle age as *"that fortunate moment when we reach the crest of a mountain. We can look back and see where we've been, and look ahead and see the inevitable descent. Meanwhile we are on the top of the mountain."* Maybe I can draw my own map to guide me forward.

4

YOU'D think that, living in Leitrim, water – or rather, the lack of it – would not be a problem. When we came to live here 18 years ago, my dad's opinion of the place was much the same as Dustin's on *The Den*. *"They've moved to Leitrim,"* he'd say, *"Leitrim, where even the snipes wear wellies!"*

When we moved into our house, we had no running water. Clothes were washed in a basin outside the front door, and brought across the fields to the stream for rinsing. We washed ourselves in a large red plastic bath in front of a roaring range. You needed two people to carry the bath outside later, for emptying. The day our instant shower was finally installed and operational, I inaugurated it by taking the first shower. I love my shower. It's the nearest I come to standing under waterfalls. Images come to me from old Sunday afternoon films. A rock pool deep in a tropical forest. A young native girl stands poised on the edge of a rock. She dives into the clear water and, surfacing, throws back her long dark hair.

Around this time last year, our group water supply had major problems. We had no running water for weeks. Dirty dishes piled up at the side of the sink, to be done all together in one fell swoop. Clothes were brought into town to the launderette. I had water on the brain: bringing water home in large plastic containers for drinking and cooking; getting water from the stream to fill the large saucepan on the range to heat for washing up, washing the floor, washing ourselves. I arrived home from work each evening, hoping and praying that the water would be back. My ears were hypersensitive to the coughs and rumbles coming from the pipes – indications that the men were on the job.

The day did come, eventually. The pipes spluttered and knocked for hours. The tap in the kitchen jumped, like a car started in gear. Then – music – the tank upstairs began to fill and, finally, out of the kitchen tap came a strong continuous flow of water. Now, all the images I associate with grace are of water.

5

I LOVE the word 'ritual' . . . the sound and taste of it on my tongue. The magic and possibilities it brings to mind. According to the *Oxford Pocket Dictionary* a ritual is: (a) prescribed order of a ceremony; (b) solemn or colourful pageantry; (c) procedure regularly followed. How cut and dried. How boring! I want to shout out, *"That is not ritual!"*

The experience of ritual can be powerful and transforming. I remember with joy celebrating *Rosh Hashana* with Jewish friends in America last September. *Rosh Hashana* is the Jewish new year. After we had all sat down to eat, the *challah* bread was brought out with ceremony and placed in the centre of the table, on the embroidered cloth. Both the bread and the meal we were about to eat had been prepared by David. He had spent all day in the kitchen. The *challah* bread was a beautiful golden colour. David took the bread and passed it to his left. One by one, each of us, adults and children, broke off a piece, then passed it on. Waiting until everyone was ready, we ate it together. The simple ritual act moved me deeply. It felt like a First Communion. That evening I ate gefilte fish for the first time. Towards the end of the meal each person present shared their hopes and desires for the coming year. Sarah, the youngest daughter, had gotten bored during dinner. She was playing under the table. I remember her whispering from beneath the tablecloth, *"I want to learn to dance."*

I want more of this sharing in my life.

RITA NORMANLY

1

OUR immediate family had not been visited by death for more than 20 years. Time had dulled the memory of how it really felt. This time, when it came again, the visit was sudden, totally unexpected. We were left reeling. Doorbells and telephones rang in the small hours. I stood at the kitchen window as streaks of dawn coloured the sky and I tried to will the sun not to rise. But the sun rose and the world kept turning and we gathered to begin our journey.

I remember a car overtaking me at speed that morning and, as it passed, a tiny bird flew from the hedge and was struck by the wing mirror. I watched the feathers scatter suddenly and drift slowly down as if in slow motion. It seemed that we were like that tiny broken bird that morning, while life continued on its way.

In the numbness of realisation and the not yet knowing how and why, we functioned automatically. A few people came and simply sat with us as we made phone calls, took phone calls and tried to absorb what had happened. Their presence was so reassuring, so important, so kind. I began to feel that somehow in all this, life was offering me some valuable lessons if I was willing to learn.

2

THE sun had set and had risen again. We had some answers to some questions, we had a plan. In the space of a few hours we had gone from normality to numbness to functioning again. We had spoken words like 'coffin' and 'funeral' and had survived. Kind people who had walked this road before offered gentle helping hands. I was learning that life does not really speed on and leave you in your brokenness. People stopped for us, with us.

We met my sister's friends, many of them for the first time, and I could put faces on familiar names. This loss was not just ours, a person belongs to life, and their passing touches many people in different ways. We brought my sister home to her own room because it felt right. What had happened had happened, and no amount of choreography or cosmetic nicety was going to make it any easier.

Death had blocked my path and stopped me in my tracks. I had to look it in the eye, I had to help my children to look it in the eye. All the wishing in the world wasn't going to make it go away. If only it could.

3

THE sun had set and risen again – it must have, but I no longer knew what day of the week it was. Life as we knew it had stopped and we had been overshadowed by this power which was much greater than all of us. I watched how we worked together, all held in that primary family bond that made our individual adult lives feel strangely distant.

On every step of that dark journey there were people – neighbours and friends around us, sitting in the kitchen, making tea, bringing food, directing traffic in the narrow boreen to the house, talking, listening, being there. Faces came from every side, kind caring faces and voices of people who had stopped to take time out to be with us. It seemed like I could read the emotions of everyone I met. Suddenly we all had become transparent, stripped of the various masks and subtle defences that we normally shelter behind. This was pure, uncensored reality.

Old stories were told, school stories, family stories, memories. Somehow they sounded truer, funnier than they had ever before and we laughed hysterically at times. All the stories, the memories, the tears, the laughter were telling me the same thing. Life never stays the same, it has its own seasons and we are like the leaves on the trees that grow, flourish and die when the time is right.

4

A BUTTERFLY danced around the flowers and the candles in the church as we let her go from this life. We stood around her grave and knew that our family was changed for ever, our lives were changed for ever. Death had stepped into a new circle and caught us unawares, not knowing how much that circle really meant. Like a grove of trees we had grown together, the roots and branches spreading in relation to each other so that the whole grove took on the outline of one tree. When one of the trees was suddenly no longer there, every other tree felt its roots and branches being tested.

Four days earlier, all of us had busy lives, commitments, plans, important things to be done. We lived in different places, even on different continents. Now we found ourselves together, all the urgency, the busy-ness put on hold, the distances overcome, because of something more important.

Death teaches us about our own mortality and shines a strong light on what's important and what's not important. Sometimes there's a high price on that lesson.

There is always time for what's important if we stop to think what that is.

5

THE summer came and went, the autumn came. I searched the night sky for reassurance. It felt as if life had moved on and forgotten us. I wanted to go into a dark cave somewhere and be alone with my loneliness for a month, then maybe I'd be ready to step back into life. There seemed to be too much sadness everywhere, too little worth smiling about.

But I was beginning to understand the lesson that life had given me. Death cannot be experienced, dealt with and packaged neatly away any more than life can, because they are the two sides of the same coin. When you touch one, you touch the other – when you deny one, you deny its power.

Another summer has come and gone and another autumn. A friend rang me and told me that a woman she works with has just lost her son. I know the road those people will have to walk now, the road that people have walked since time began and will walk until the end of time. The shadowy road that I stepped onto a few seasons ago when life decided it was time for me to learn a few lessons from death.

When you walk for a while in the shadows, you learn a lot about the light and there is always light.

MARY O'MALLEY

1

SAY you downed tools this minute and decided not to go to work, not to mind the children, to forget about the washing-up, the new tyre for the car. Say if you're a woman you decide to escape for the day from whatever sweet emotional dictatorship you serve, be it lover or children or husband. And if you're a man you slip whatever unfathomable moorings anchor you to the practical, the cut and thrust of job, family, serving the tiger.

You may be uneasy with your gender. You might, in which case your main escape route is inwards, be in jail. You may have no job, no home, no welcome, holding such notions only in your memory, encased in what dreams you have left. If you are listening to this, you have some idea of the shape of your day. Suppose you changed it? And say you were to set out instead this morning on a pilgrimage, where would it be? Not Lough Derg nor the Reek, nor Graceland, not the Louvre, nor that house in Paris where Piaf awoke and sipped her morning coffee. None of those yet, but somewhere sacred to memory, a house where you once lived maybe, or a flat with French windows in a big city in another country when everything was still possible. Would it be a strand in Ballyferriter, or the river you swam in when you first fell in love? If there were a snatch of music, what would it be? Verdi? Some early Beethoven? Ó Riada, possibly, or something from the swamps of Louisiana with a Cajun swing?

You can't go. Of course not. Not today. But if not today, why not tomorrow or next week? You couldn't possibly? But it's up to you – it's your morning, isn't it?

2

IN his brilliant trilogy on the island of Arainn, Tim Robinson has borrowed the Stations of the Cross as the outer form his peregrination will take. But at the end of *Pilgrimage* he writes, *"But for a book to stand like an island out of the sea of the unwritten it must acknowledge its own bounds, and turn in from them, and look into the labyrinth."* As a child, I loved the Stations of the Cross. Those poor reproductions of Italian painters in their ornate wooden frames, from what school or period I still don't know, were my first introduction to art, and to the redemptive power of suffering. That there were dangers in such dark ecstasies for young girls appeared to escape an otherwise vigilant clergy. Who else, in the small church in Ballyconneely with its beautiful Italianate marble altar (since removed in the name of dubious modernity), looked for longer than the required Hail Mary, Our Father and Gloria, their gaze drawn out from the image of Christ's agony through a marble colonnade onto an olive grove on the slopes of the Tuscan or Florentine hills, and upwards to the intense blue of an Italian sky.

Those 14 steps described, and inscribed in our bodies, a ritual that remains powerful and outlasts the faith they commemorated. Outlasts the faith but not the passion, nor the image of Veronica.

So I stopped at each station and believed that this was what was needed for salvation. Now, however, I know all such journeys must, sooner or later, admit the limitations of their outer shape and turn, inevitably, inwards on an unavoidable quest, for some flame or flicker, the occasional torch we might hold aloft against the dark like a bunch of yellow furze. And on that spiralling odyssey, Catholic practice and Greek mythology sometimes inevitably collide, and occasionally mesh.

3

L AST week I went to Inis Mór Arainn to spend unfettered
time on the island. For too long I have been there on writing-
related business, meeting friends and the island writers in the
process, but always returning on the morning ferry. This time I
had only one purpose – to walk. I also hoped to meet friends,
hear music – which happened, but not by appointment. I took a
walk inland that would have taken me to the village of Gort na
gCapaill had I been more sure of myself, or trusted maps. I have
a curious relationship with maps and am full of admiration for
people who use them, and for whom they appear to work.
Perhaps an early orienteering episode, when upwards of 40
girls in gymslips got hopelessly lost in the Twelve Bens along
with our cohort of nuns, is partly to blame. Anyhow, a German
with a map of the cliffs sent me the wrong way, blinding me
with useless information, and thus reinforced a number of
prejudices at once. A local man put me right in terms I
understood, *"follow this path, to that cliff, on that outcrop"*. I got to
the great pool of Poll na bPeist easily. And I got to thinking, as
you do with the sea pounding up against the cliffs, about the
boy Micheleen Dillane, star of the film *Man of Aran*, who
disappeared in Dunkirk's aftermath and was never heard from
again.

There is a danger in being appointed to represent a culture by
those that want us to be actors in their particular vision of our
lives; in what they think they would like us to have come from
or become. Too often, people perish living up to someone else's
dream. A bit like children with parents who can't or won't let
go.

4

ACCORDING to legend, Galway was built on the site of the drowning of Galvia, the river-goddess, and as a result of her extended waking. This is a temple of youth, where every whim of entertainment, dress and drug-of-choice is catered for. Walk into Galway any night at 10 o'clock and the streets are alive with revellers. Young people spill from the doorways of every pub and restaurant in a town devoted to festivity. Even in winter before the start of the festivals, which now seem to constitute the town's main industry.

Despite the occasional ugly incident, this is a safe place. What seems remarkable to me is not the rowdiness of the crowds, but their complaisance – no protest marches, no demonstrations, very little civil unrest even among the students, whose first duty, surely, is to flout all authority, loudly and often and with great heat. The atmosphere in the streets is neither jaded nor joyous, though there is a touch of both; it is more the sense of application. Pleasure is pursued with the kind of dogged studiousness usually reserved for exams, and an almost equal predictability. This town is the advertiser's dream.

But this is a town built on real dreams of pleasure and delight, on hope and youth and possibility, as well as the burgher's city it has always been and by whose precepts it now conducts itself. Perhaps we owe our children the frame of slight constraint, the small deprivations and challenges they need to test themselves, because this is above all the age of trying themselves out.

"Through a chink too wide, no wonder enters," wrote Patrick Kavanagh – and it is worth reflecting on this sentiment from a man damaged and embittered by an Ireland where social and intellectual freedom was regarded as a dangerous perversion. Perhaps the pendulum, in its wild swing, has deprived us of wonder along with shame. The question is whether this is a necessary price for freedom and how it will be paid and by whom.

5

THEY stream out of the lecture halls and schoolrooms like brightly coloured birds, flitting and wheeling and hopping along the concourse and corridors, and sometimes I watch them, delighted by their physical grace and think they are all beautiful at this age. They can do anything – nothing is beyond their grasp, those Leaving Cert and college students, the lucky ones.

Why is it then that we ask so little of them, content to herd them prematurely into safe professions where the dollar and pound dot the bottom-line like so many bullet holes. Why turn them out alike as those little cocktail sausages they will soon buy frozen in the supermarket, before they graduate to sushi. This morning, on your way to work, look at them, the young. Aren't they taller, better dressed, more sure of themselves than we were? Less desperate. At least on the surface. We know the surface is just that – a shiny screen to reflect what we want them to be. Or what their friends, the multinationals, the marketing executives, themselves terrifically young want from them.

Underneath the flat surface there is something more interesting going on, alongside the doubts and troubles and agony of the first broken love affairs. Shouldn't we, the teachers and doctors and writers and parents, be interested in this? Shouldn't we at least try to find out how they feel, what kind of heart beats under the bright plumage of those sleek young Europeans we are rearing, before we trust them to the mercy of the Common Market and the common currency and the commonplace? They will not all make it in the world we have fashioned for them. So take a good look – at a bent head, an upturned face, the heart-stopping beauty of your barely adult son or daughter. Take a mental photograph and hold it, tucked into your sleeve or the crook of your elbow or the pocket of a skirt. Hold on to it through the day. You never know how much you will depend on it.

JOE O'SHEA

1

AS a child of the 1980s, I never thought I would catch myself starting a sentence with, *"Kids these days – huh!"* At least not for another year or two. But there I was recently railing against our current generation of teens, as myself and an old school friend reminisced about that topsy-turvy decade that saw us venture out into the world.

It's hard to believe it now, but of my Leaving Cert year of about 35 guys who left our school in Cork in the summer of 1987, only five or six were still at home by Christmas.

For most of us, it was a case of, *"Where are you going to go - Boston, London or Sydney?"* Looking back, I reckon the college entry forms, the CAOs, should have had a separate box where you could tick off your exile destination of choice. Those were the days of mass emigration and staying in touch through long letters with exotic postmarks. I've lost touch with most of them by now – of course – and I expect that few of us would recognise each other in the street.

It's not so long ago, but really it was a different world then, before emails and satellite TV. These days, you can chat live to friends on the other side of the world, or catch the big GAA games and soccer internationals that meant so much to us when we were so far from home. I'm not saying that the fact my generation had to deal with mass emigration made us any better than those who followed in more prosperous times, but I do envy them the fact that they have the choice of staying closer to home and friends while studying or starting to work. Of course, looking back with regrets is a bit previous when you are still in your early thirties. And I should look on the bright side – at least I can bore the pants off younger colleagues with tales of how it *"were right tough when I were a lad"*.

2

CLOTHES may maketh the man but it is by his accent that he will surely be judged. A lot of Dubliners, for instance, are under the impression that anybody who does not speak with a true-blue Dub accent must have spent his childhood milking cows and threatening city-types with pitchforks. As far as they are concerned, if you don't sound like Joe Duffy, you are a dyed-in-the-wool muck savage.

Having grown up in the narrow streets of the South Parish in Cork, it was a bit annoying for me when I first landed in Baile Átha Cliath. Any time the conversation turned to, say, silage, the Dubs in the room would turn to me as if I was the oracle of all things fodder-related. It didn't matter that most of these urbanites came from such well-known urban ghettos as Foxrock, Howth or Greystones – east was east and west was west, and that was that.

I became a keen student of accents, learning to tell a Carlow man from a Tipp-ite and a Donegal girl from an Armagh lass. But the more I listened, the more my own fine Cork accent was neutralised. And, after 10 years away from the Lee, my accent is sort of halfway between Mallow and Portlaoise. But I'm not the only one who has been undergoing a transformation. From the start of the 1990s, many suburban Dubs were beginning to affect the truly atrocious DART accent – a terrible take on the English home-counties voice usually heard when rugger fans are ordering a pint of 'Heino'. And even friends from the more rustic parts of the country were also adopting increasingly neutral tones.

I have decided that the drive for bland accents coincided with the rise in our economic fortunes. When we didn't have a pot to pee in between us, the way we talked was not a major issue and people knew it was pointless to put on airs and graces. But now that the money is rolling in – we have the right accent to go with the right car and the right type of pine flooring.

It's a real pity, for two reasons. Firstly, we are in danger of losing the richness of our daily language, and, secondly, there are few things scarier than a Cavan man attempting a Dublin 4 accent.

3

WHEN I'm on my travels around Ireland, I can always tell when I drive into a Tidy Town. The first thing you see is the immaculately manicured grass verge taking over from the overgrown ditches on the side of the road. Then there is the 'Welcome' sign, usually carved out of wood or made of chiselled granite with the name of the town in fussy script. Next come the brightly coloured homes, the overflowing window boxes and the traditional shop-front signs in old Irish script. Everything's neat and tidy and every agricultural implement within a five-mile radius has been dragged out into the main street and given a lick of paint.

I never spend too long in these tidy villages, partly because I'm afraid that, if I leave the car parked for five minutes, somebody will give it a coat of emulsion and hang a window box off the boot.

It may sound sour, but these towns always strike me as slightly spooky and very kitsch. They are uniformly cute in a Stepford Wives sort of way. They remind me of those old John Hinde post-cards with over-bright colours that positively shout at you. You half expect to find the main street clogged with rosy-cheeked young boys in *geansaís*, driving donkeys with turf-loaded creels. At any minute, John Wayne may come busting through the doors of the pub – in hot pursuit of Maureen O'Hara. There's one village in West Cork in particular that always makes me think that, if Liberace had been born an Irishman, this would have been his hometown. One of the few things you can say for the Tidy Towns look is that, if Hollywood ever wants to remake *The Quiet Man* or *Brigadoon,* they won't be short of locations.

It may sound churlish to do down what is undoubtedly a lot of effort by a lot of people, but, speaking purely from an aesthetic point of view, there has to be a happy medium, some way we can tone down the prettification and the cutesiness. After all, even in the most rustic times of old, no town in Ireland looked anything like the typical Tidy Town. Most of our towns and villages have enough character and quirkiness to stand on their own merits. We don't need to tart them up in fake tan and a cheap dress.

4

TEXANS are fond of saying that 'God, guts and guns' made their state great. For us Irish, at least those of us who grew up in the 1970s, it was beards, bodhráns and bangers. Those were the days of the great Irish banger. Grown-ups drove slightly knackered Opel Record, tired old Cortinas and tricked-up Escorts with green sun-strips across the top of the windscreen. The typical banger sat low on knackered suspension struts, had an exhaust held on by chicken wire and a colour scheme in hint-of-rust brown. Rusted-out floor panels were patched up with whatever came to hand, with USA biscuit tins proving to be popular with the DIY panel beater. We used to sit on the wall in Crosshaven in Cork and watch the Beetles, Minors and Hillman Hunters pulling into the village with their exhaust pipes scraping along the ground. Entire extended families would then emerge like clowns getting out of a circus car.

These days, of course, the banger is an endangered species, thanks to ever-tightening road regulations. I suspect that the new generation of motorists has a false sense of total security behind their airbags, crumple zones and side impact bars. It's easy to forget that you are basically riding around in a rocket-propelled tin can. And this dangerous sense of invulnerability, together with sound systems that overwhelm the senses, may account for much of the lunatic driving on our roads. I firmly believe that the old bangers actually prevented far more accidents than they caused. There was nothing like driving around in a rusted-out Mini to encourage a strong sense of your own mortality.

5

I WAS down at the Rose of Tralee recently and witnessed a very curious sight – not that they are thin on the ground during Rose week. A live band was playing on one of the side streets in the town and a large group of local teenagers was watching from outside a pub across the road. Most of them were not drinking and were just standing around in self-conscious groups, nodding in time to the music and tapping their feet. Then a large group of Spanish kids arrived and, without any hesitation, started to do an exuberant line-dance in front of the previously ignored band. The young Spaniards spent an hour dancing and generally whooping it up, girls and boys mixing with ease and grace. The Irish kids reacted with a mix of embarrassment and a sort of uneasy 'would you look at the state of them' attitude. I got the feeling that the local teens would have loved to join in, but were terrified of the likely reaction of their peers.

It's a great pity that our young people are mostly terrified of stepping out of line in public, of making a holy show of themselves. And I'm convinced that this is one of the main reasons behind the abuse of drink by our teens. It's as if they can't let themselves go in public without having over-indulged in Dutch courage first. What should be natural youthful exuberance becomes messy acting-up that often ends in tears and feelings of guilt the next morning. The rapid move towards mixed education should help our kids to become more confident in social settings. But surely we can play a part too – and encourage our kids to get out there and enjoy the dance.

JOHN O'SHEA

1

ZAIRE, 1994, and we were witnessing Rwanda's second tragedy. After the genocide of the early summer – when up to a million Tutsis lost their lives – an outbreak of cholera in the Hutu camps was claiming further thousands of victims by the day.

The camps needed water and there was plenty of it available nearby in Lake Kivu. All that was missing was a way of bringing it from the lake to the people.

I sat one evening in that first week of the cholera outbreak and spoke about our problems with Sam Kiley, a journalist with the London *Times*. Up against a deadline, Sam was typing on his computer as the interview continued. Fifteen minutes later, his article was finished and, hooking up the computer to a satellite phone, he was able to send it to London immediately.

Sitting by the shores of Lake Kivu, we were both struck by the depth of the failure which was unfolding in front of us. Sam Kiley could send a story from central Africa to London's Fleet Street in a matter of seconds. Having failed to act to limit the scale of the genocide in April, the international community now couldn't take water from a lake and truck it 50 miles up the road to prevent massive loss of life.

There was an evil at work in Rwanda in those years, an evil which turned ordinary men into butchers. But for all that has been written about genocide, much less has been heard about our own failure to act, to make resources available to stem this tide of suffering. If there are lessons to be learned from Rwanda, perhaps the most important one is this – the world has the means, the resources and the technology to prevent large-scale loss of human life, to tackle poverty and to limit suffering. All that is lacking is the will.

2

IT'S always difficult to explain injustice to an Irish child. Sheltered from the adult world, most of them won't ever have experienced greed or cruelty, and so they simply can't understand how suffering is allowed to continue.

Returning from the Ethiopian famine of 1984, having witnessed scenes of heartbreaking sadness, I had resolved to speak to anyone I could about that country's plight. One of the first invitations in my door was one asking me to speak to a class of young children in a school in Skerries.

A day or two later, I found myself in front of a group of six- and seven-year-olds, explaining as simply as I could how millions of people were starving to death in Ethiopia because their crops had failed, and how the world was doing very little to help.

Suddenly, a little lad piped up from the middle of the class. *"My da,"* he said, *"is a fisherman, and I can ask him to go to Ethiopia and bring some children back here so we can feed them. There's loads of boats in Skerries, and if everyone with a boat did the same thing, we could save everyone,"* he suggested.

Having witnessed the scale of the suffering in Ethiopia just a week earlier, and the seeming indifference of the international community to it, I was bowled over by the boy's suggestion. It wasn't boats that were needed, but planes of food and – like boats in Skerries – there was no shortage of them. All that was lacking was the international will to pay for it.

Maybe we can all learn a lot about charity from the very young. If children don't understand adult injustices, this may not be simple innocence on their part. Perhaps, as world-weary adults, we need to look into our own hearts and search once more for that pure sense of right and wrong that we all once had.

3

SOMALIA in the summer of 1992 was as close as I've seen to hell on earth. Struggling to save lives in a country gripped by famine is a desperately difficult task, but, when you are surrounded by the threat of violence every minute of the day, the situation becomes almost intolerable. In Somalia, death was everywhere, but it seemed as if the world didn't care.

If you're not a medic, working in a famine zone can be doubly difficult. Faced with a starving child, you feel utterly helpless. All you can do is watch while groups of Irish doctors and nurses work their magic, day and night, week after week. In truth, I was glad to be leaving the northern city of Baidoa that summer's evening, having talked my way onto a cargo flight returning to Kenya. From there, I could return to Dublin and begin to raise awareness about Somalia's plight.

The only other passenger on the plane that evening was a doctor from the Arab League, a man who himself was clearly distressed by the scale of Somalia's suffering and the world's failure to respond to it. We had been talking for an hour or more when he asked, *"Where are you from?"* *"Ireland,"* I said. *"Ah,"* he responded, smiling, *"the caring nation."*

Twenty-five thousand feet above Somalia, away from the misery, the suffering and death, I felt deeply moved. For so many people around the world, the Irish are legendary drinkers, great storytellers, natural comics, but in Somalia, where it mattered most, we were the ones who cared.

None of the Irish doctors and nurses who worked in Somalia had to leave the security of their homes – none of them were forced to risk their lives in the Horn of Africa so that others might survive – but they came and worked without pay because they cared about the plight of their fellow human beings.

Almost a decade on, as the roar of the Celtic Tiger drowns out all other voices, I look back with pride at that time when we gained the respect of the world not because we were successful, but because we cared.

4

THE mass in a small church hidden amid Calcutta's slums began at 4.30 am, but I felt obliged to make it there on time. Promised a lift with the Missionaries of Charity to a leper colony in Tanager, some three hours outside the city, I felt that joining them in prayer as the day began was the least I could do.

The mass over, I hung around the yard outside, waiting for my lift and wondering what an Irish sports journalist could discuss with an Indian nun for three hours in a car. I needn't have worried. My companion for the journey was Mother Teresa, and I spent the rest of the day in awe, watching this small woman who had enough love for everyone she met.

That day was about 21 years ago now, but it has had a lasting effect on me. It was my first trip to Calcutta and, surrounded by what seemed to be an unending tide of misery, I began to despair. In the nightmare of Calcutta's slums, it seemed as if the only release was death. Sickened by the sight of so much poverty, I approached Mother Teresa. *"When you work in these conditions every day, surrounded by so much suffering,"* I said, *"do you ever stop and wonder if you're making some kind of impact on poverty?"* She turned to me and smiled, saying, *"Every day of my life in Calcutta, I make it my business to lift a leper or a dying person or a child in desperate need and hug and kiss that person. I don't know whether that is the best thing to do for that person but I do know it's the right thing to do."*

Twenty-one years later, I still feel privileged at the opportunity I had that day. Amid the dirt and the dying in Calcutta's slums, in the depths of the most appalling poverty, I witnessed the power of love, and its ability to light up even the darkest places.

5

SHOESHINE boys are on the lowest rung of the ladder in the Third World – almost always homeless, and often as young as five or six years old, they eke out a miserable living on the streets of every African capital. By day, they aim to make enough to keep hunger at bay; at night, they sleep together in small groups in doorways or disused buildings.

The young boy who shone my shoes in Freetown, the capital of Sierra Leone, that day was no different. Barefooted and clothed in rags, he couldn't have been more than nine or ten years old. Without the chance of education, he was doomed to spend the rest of his life on these streets and, most probably, to die on them.

My shoes shined, I stood up and paid the young lad before walking on into the city. Fifteen minutes later, arriving at the door of my hotel, I heard a shout and looked around to see the shoeshine boy running after me. Perspiration dripping from his forehead, he held out his hand with a smile. He was holding my wallet, which I must have dropped by his stall earlier.

One of the most extraordinary things about this story is that I was due to fly the following day to Guinea to buy supplies for a project we had just opened, and as a result I was carrying at least $5,000 in my wallet. The notes were bulging out of the sides. This boy had found more money than he could ever dream of making in his entire working life and he was offering to give it back to me. He didn't have enough money to buy shoes, but he hadn't touched a note in the wallet.

The Third World is full of contradictions, but none more striking than this: in the midst of some of the worst poverty, you can discover the greatest human qualities.

COLIN O'SULLIVAN

1

WHY does she weep so? Hard to know.Perhaps she always weeps so. She is an old bow-legged woman and she walks Apple Road every day. The sun in northern Japan is hot, a scorching August. It's hot reaching to the bending boughs of her husband's orchard. He died, she works. Sometimes tears get confused with perspiration.

In the morning, her body smells like tea: fine, dry, the canister opened. Jasmine or oolong. In the evening it is of old vegetables, boiling long in a small kitchen. Boiling, boiling to the point when vegetables break and tear from too much heat and moisture. Ravaged.

The orchards of Aomori prefecture are filled with stooped women in protective headcloths. She is only one of them. If you talk to her, she will tell you that toil on this soil puts food in the children's mouths and toil makes them who they are. If you ask her why she weeps, she will say there are no tears, only perspiration, and when the sun catches this it is a rainbow.

2

SHE had won her race and that was all.

She had struggled so long to become an internationally renowned runner and now she stood on a podium, gold medal
resplendent in the sun. Her national anthem sounded, boister-
ous; the flag, red sun centred on a white background, flew above
her. She did not understand debates about nationalism, divinity, politics; she had run her race and that was all.

Her coach had been hard. He had told her that she didn't have
any style. But she knew that a young girl on a racetrack had no
need for style. Style was for the nightclubs of Tokyo, the girls of
Roppongi and Shinjuku. She knew only of desire.

She didn't understand fully the history lessons of school, didn't
consider the depths of words like *kamikaze*. But she knew where
the finish line was and how to get there. Her coach was right,
she didn't have any style. Commentators would say no substance either. But she knew she had desire and could represent
her country by this desire. She had won her race and that was
all.

3

YOU speak little of my language. I speak less of yours. But I return every week to your bar, walking down a road, a nameless road and unsignposted, I find you, and find you as always in good form. Your bar is a *yakitori* bar. *Yakitori* is the simplest of Japanese dishes – meat, usually chicken, grilled on little bamboo skewers. Every week you serve this food to me on a little plate, and a warm towel to wipe my hands. You know I like the liver *yakitori* best, and you know when my beer needs refilling, even when your back is turned. I always bow to you first, master of the house.

The *gaijin*, or foreigners, come to you. Sometimes your bar brims with American accents, English accents, the tongues of Australia or Canada. And they bow to you, joke with you. They call you Bob, because it's easy for them. And you seem to like being called Bob. And all these friends will learn your language, even if it's just a few words. Just to be able to say we respect you and appreciate you making us feel comfortable in a foreign land. Just to be able to say thank you.

4

THE snow monkey creeps into the other side of the hot spring bath. In Hokkaido, the northernmost island of Japan, they sometimes do this.

Hokkaido is cold, bitter, and the hot spring bath, or *onsen*, is a warm refuge. The girl sees the monkey. They see each other. Fine snowflakes fall on their heads but they remain warm, up to their necks in natural bliss.

Although at opposite sides of the bath, they can still peer through the steam and find each other's eyes. They stare. At first she is afraid. Primate, primal. But the water on her shoulders, the smell of old wood, steam and steam . . . and she relaxes. When the monkey drops his shoulders she finds herself doing the same. When he rotates his neck, oozing relief, she follows suit. When he stares, she stares.

Hours, or minutes, later the monkey lifts himself out of the *onsen* a nd scurries back into the snow. Then her boyfriend returns. When he removes his robe and steeps himself beside her she tells him that she is no longer afraid and that yes, yes she will marry him.

5

OUTSIDE their little homes, old men sit, stoking a little fire. It is summer in Japan and it is *Obon*, the festival of the dead. For three or four days, relatives return to this world to be with their families. The first fires are there to welcome the visitors.

During this time of year, families prefer to stay at home. They sit respectfully low at the table, careful to place their chopsticks in a correct manner. You don't want to offend the dead, especially when they sit so close to you.

These are a solemn few days, though the people smile. They are glad to have their dead, beloved relatives in the home and, although they cannot see them, their smiles are enough to acknowledge their presence.

It is the last night, and an old man dressed in his *yukata*, his traditional summer wear, sits on a chair at his doorstep. There he stokes the embers gently; the last flames have bid them safe return to the spirit world.

He smiles to himself, he enjoyed the company. He is hoping that next year he will be able to welcome them again, and he is also safe in the knowledge that they are prepared to welcome him.

JONATHAN PHILBIN BOWMAN

1

ONE of the great things about my life and about my work, which are the same thing really, is that I get to meet all kinds of people. People at every level and people in all kinds of businesses – actors and people who do different things with their lives. By chance last week I met a director of the Central Bank. It's a pretty important job and we chatted away about life and possibility and what you could do. And we came up with some ideas about things one might do. He said, *"What about the people who have no choice?"* He meant the little people. People who don't have a company car. People who don't have £60,000 and a big house in Foxrock. And I said, *"What people have no choice?"* And he said, *"Well, you know, people who are in jobs they hate."* And I said, *"They* have *a choice. All the time. All the time. Every minute of your life you have a choice. Every second. Every instant you have a choice, right?"* And he said, "No, no they have to work." And I said, *"No, no they might* choose *to work in a job they hate and they might* choose *to spend what little free time they have going out on a Friday together and having beer, complaining to one another how awful the job is, and how awful the boss is. But that's a choice. The only time you don't have a choice is when they're actually nailing you to the cross. When there are two guys hammering nails into your hands, and two guys hammering nails into your feet. And even then you have a choice, because you have a choice to forgive them, you've a choice to be a victim, you've a choice to feel the pain, you've a choice to think about your last supper."*

2

ONE of the most beautiful women I ever met is called Nigella Lawson. Her father used to be Chancellor of the Exchequer under Margaret Thatcher: Nigel Lawson. She's married to a man called John Diamond who has cancer and he's lost his tongue. He only gurgles, but she can translate. Her sister died of breast cancer. Her mother died of breast cancer, so she has to be screened every year. Her husband is a little older than her, and she's got two children called Cosima and Bruno, three and five, and they're beautiful.

I was in her book-lined house. They're refitting the kitchen and John is kinda funny about this because he knows he won't be there, necessarily, to see the end of the kitchen being refitted. But still he makes his input and makes his decisions. And in the course of our interview, she said, *"If I wanted to be rich I'd have gone into the City, but I'm lucky because, this way, I can follow my interests and I can do what I like to do. I like writing in this way, I'm so lucky."*

I called up the next day and I said, *"Nigella, I know why you're lucky, I understand, but my readers will not understand. How can you say, with your husband dying of cancer and all of that, how can you say you're lucky? And how can you, as a food writer for* Vogue, *how can you search for the right asparagus? It's so trivial. Or is it that those small things are what count?"* And she said, *"Yeah. I think it's only in its tiniest moments that we most deeply experience life."*

3

MY friend Susan gives seminars around the world and she asks people to put up their hands and she says, "*How many people believe in God?*" Maybe half the hands go up because these are kinda New-Age types, so many of them are atheists or agnostics, or God knows what. Well God *would* know what exactly. Anyway, then she says, "*Okay, of all those of you who believe in God, how many of you* trust *God?*" The answer is not very many. Why exactly would you need to buy insurance if you trusted God? Anyway, the whole thing about God is this: I don't know why people need miracles to prove anything. It seems to me that fingernails are a miracle. The fact that, if you're lucky and your child is okay, they get born with five on each hand. Fingernails! I mean who came up with fingernails and put them just there at the end and let them grow and made them hard and different chemically from flesh? That's enough of a miracle. There's enough in the world to be in awe of.

4

NOTHING should be compulsory (especially not Irish) and of course, the secret is, nothing *is* compulsory. But if you've got kids in school you should give them a day off from time to time for no reason. Like even when they don't ask. And go play with them. The world is an adventure. Go have an adventure. My son often says to me, *"Dad, are we going home now or can we have an adventure?"* And we go and we have adventures. And you can have adventures too. Having a kid is a pretty good excuse. If you don't have a kid, have adventures anyway. But the thing is this: boredom is when you're not learning.

5

HOW I became a journalist. It was completely by accident.
I saw Quentin Crisp on the *Late Late Show*. (That was
when Gay Byrne used to do the *Late Late Show*.) And I wanted to
meet him; I was about 16 or 17. So I had a friend in college who
was doing a magazine and I said, *"Do you want an interview with
Quentin Crisp?"* And he said, *"Yeah."* So I phoned up the theatre and I said I wanted to do an interview with Quentin Crisp
for this magazine and it was the first interview I ever did. Also,
perhaps the last interview I did with Quentin Crisp might have
been the last *he* ever did, because I met him last year, shortly
before he died. I went back to check and he said, *"Of course I
don't remember you but it always amazes me that people are obsessed
with the idea that I should remember them. What should matter is that
you want to be with them and spend time with them and take pleasure
in their company."* Anyway, he used to have lunch every day in
the same café in New York and we were joined by this gay,
confused, English kid of about 20, I'd say. And afterwards we
went for some drinks in a pub called The Jonathan Swift and
the kid said to him, *"What's the meaning of life?"* And Crisp said,
"Happiness." And the kid says, *"What's the secret of happiness?"*
And Quentin Crisp says, after a pause, and this is what every
wise Buddha would say, *"The secret of happiness is remaining in
your mind and in your body in the present moment for as long as is
humanly possible."*

JACK PREGER

1

IN Calcutta, where I work with the poor, Radio Éireann is rarely heard. So I don't know how many previous *Living Word* programmes have referred to St John's Gospel. My justification is that St John gives us a message of supreme, mystical importance.

> *"In the beginning was the Word and the Word was with God and the Word was God. The same was in the beginning with God."*

I once owned a farm in Wales, north of Fishguard. One winter's day, as I was carting muck on land overlooking the sea, I felt my head was being opened and a thought put in – 'become a doctor'. And then the head was closed with that order inside it. So I applied to medical schools.

But how to sell the farm was a real problem. And then I had another strange idea. On a very clear day, it was possible to see Ireland and I thought, *"I won't sell until I've seen Ireland."* Whenever I was with the sheep, out on the cliffs, I looked across. In vain. But then one day I took a friend to Fishguard to catch the London train. I had applied to Trinity College medical school and at Fishguard there was a boat leaving for Rosslare. After phoning back to the farm, I was on the boat, almost penniless, bound for Dublin. I hitch-hiked from Rosslare, sleeping in a barn. From Trinity I was sent to College of Surgeons. And Surgeons accepted me. *Deo gratias.*

2

I STUDIED medicine in College of Surgeons from 1965 and lodged at 33 Synge Street, Shaw's birthplace. The house was full of UCD agriculture students, who went home in the Christmas vacation whilst I stayed on. Only to find that, as the weather got colder, the blankets on the bed got fewer. With the reduced rents, our beloved landlady, Mrs Giblin, pawned the blankets and there was no hope of respite until the vacation ended.

At the church nearby, however, Father Tonge introduced me to a belief that made up for the sufferings at the lodgings and the difficulties of the medical course. If the Holy Spirit wants something done, someone, somewhere, will get the push to do it. And certainly I got pushed to Bangladesh to work as a doctor in the refugee camps after the 1971 war. Even though I was about to accept a job in a Jamaican hospital.

After seven years in Bangladesh, I was expelled due to my having exposed an international traffic in children involving government officials. So I set up Calcutta Rescue, working with the poor in Calcutta for the next 20 years. We now have five free clinics, three schools and two vocational training centres.

If Father Tonge were alive today, he would see Calcutta Rescue's work as confirmation of his belief in the workings of the Holy Spirit. The spirit ordered; I obeyed.

3

IN Calcutta, recently, I was summoned to testify in the canonisation process of Mother Teresa, with whose order I have had medical dealings since 1972. When the testifying was over, a former volunteer of Mother's sent me the Liam Fay book *Beyond Belief*. In Calcutta, if Fay were to attempt a demolition job on Mother Teresa, all communities would regard him as another Salman Rushdie. It says a great deal for Irish tolerance that Fay could publish and republish his assessments of Irish Catholicism and live to tell the tale.

Since Mother Teresa died, the search is on for post-mortem miracles. The Canadian priest with the Polish name I cannot attempt to pronounce has received enough reports to keep Fay happy for many a day. If we look at Rushdie's writings before *The Satanic Verses*, we see gratuitous insults and ridicule directed at Christianity and Buddhism which evoked no public reaction. With Fay we get a rag-bag of hilarious religious headcases plus some courageous debunking of religious experiences among the ostensibly sane. Then there is Christopher Hitchens writing on Mother Teresa's alleged shortcomings in *The Missionary Position*. But these writers have quite forgotten the parable of the Baby and the Bathwater. If the word of God is to survive we *need* these debunkers, writers with the courage, like Fay, to go to Coolock and examine the woodwork to see if Christ had appeared therein. That way we may find the real 'living word', with the absurdities removed. *Ad gloriam Dei*.

4

I AM writing this on my travels, from Calcutta to Holland, to attend the annual meeting of Calcutta Rescue, the charity I work for. I broke my journey in Amman and have spent a week in Jerusalem. The devotion of the faithful – Christian, Muslim and Jewish – is impressive but appears fanatical at times. The various shrines have a beauty beyond expression, but it is vital to understand what Jerusalem is really about. It is not about a Jewish temple on which mosques have been built. The Jewish Holy of Holies is lost somewhere below these Arab mosques. Nor is it about the various alternative locations at which Christ may have been tried and crucified. There are now Jewish archaeologists who are called 'minimalists' because, the more they dig, the less they find to confirm the Old Testament histories. I visited Hebron's Tombs, but only God knows who is buried there, since no evidence exists in the history of the matriarchs and patriarchs, like Sarah or Abraham.

I believe that, if God's word is to live amongst us, we need to examine the fact – what we have in *fact*, rather than in myth. We must deduce from past mythology what may have been the spiritual reality. Our world may survive for billions of years, according to cosmologists. How long will our current beliefs last?

5

IN this my final *Living Word* talk, I leave you with a few heresies. The word of God I live by in Calcutta does not correspond with current doctrines. In 1974, at the time of the Pentecost (although I was unaware of the Church calendar), I was staying in Dawson's Lodge on the Castle Leslie demesne in Glaslough, County Monaghan. For a single moment the Paraclete announced itself to me. Not as a voice, but as a thought – *"I am the Paraclete"*. I had no idea what the Paraclete was, but my body felt a freshness I only remember from my childhood. My mind felt as though it was totally without tension. The dictionary told me that this was the Holy Spirit.

Working with the poor in Bengal since 1972, I have been faced with mothers whose children were lost. An established market exists for such children, the chances of recovery are slight. For three children I prayed at length to Mary the Mother of Christ. Eventually, each child was found, to the amazement of many, myself especially. No heresy here.

But I believe only in the one God, present in our lives as the Paraclete. Or the Jewish Shechina. No virgin birth, no only begotten son, no third day resurrection. I see Christ as a divinely inspired prophet within some of whose reported teachings lies our salvation. When Christians, Muslims and Jews accept this, we may have some peace.

DAVID RICE

1

I WILL never forget the first moment I became aware of the sun on a green field at evening time. I was a boy of 15, walking through a grassy field in County Armagh. Suddenly the sun came through the clouds and its rays, coming towards me, touched the field in front of me. The field began to glow and became a magical yellow-green, and it was startlingly beautiful.

I plucked a blade of grass and held it up. It was then I realised that the sunlight was not just reflecting off it, but was driving through the blade of grass and lighting it up like a tiny flame. And its colour had changed to that same magical yellow-green.

Then I understood that the field itself had become millions of those tiny yellow-green flames. Every blade of grass was aglow. The field was on fire with sunlight. Ever since then, evening fields have glowed for me and, when I point them out to my friends, they start seeing them too.

Some years later I was on an FCA route march in County Kildare. Our route took us through a wood, where the order was given to halt and stand at ease. I remember looking up at the beech trees over my head, and seeing for the first time how every leaf lit up as the sunlight filtered through. Each leaf had become a tiny stained-glass window.

We sing about our 'forty shades of green'. Those are only two of them, but all down the years they have brought joy to me. Take a look for yourself.

Helen Keller once said the greatest tragedy is to have eyes and not to see.

Lord, that I may see.

2

DO you remember as a child lying on the ground and looking up at the top of a tall tree? And as the clouds rushed past, it seemed as if the tree was toppling over. I did it again the other day, and the trees are still toppling and the clouds still rushing.

The sky is the greatest show on earth – a gigantic canvas on which God (or nature) paints the most magnificent abstract paintings, wipes them out and starts all over again.

The other day, I was watching a flat line of clouds scudding across the horizon at twilight. The spike of the crescent moon came up out of the vapour, and as it sliced through the scudding cloud it was the dorsal fin of a great white shark.

A while ago a couple of us were watching a sunset from the Cliffs of Moher. Suddenly a mist enveloped us, and the whole mist turned rose pink. Everyone fell silent with the magic of being inside a rose-pink world.

Did you ever watch a cloud disappear? Gaze at a wisp of cloud in a blue sky, and often you will see it get thinner and more ethereal, and then suddenly it is gone.

When did you last focus binoculars on a starry sky? What you see is frightening – the sheer immensity of those numbers of silent stars.

Oscar Wilde in *The Ballad of Reading Gaol* spoke of *"that little tent of blue which prisoners call the sky"*. But if I am not a prisoner, the sky is all mine. That is if I bother to notice it.

Lord, that I may see.

3

THERE is a tiny remote bay in Donegal, just around the headland from Glencolumcille, where the seashore has the most exquisite rounded stones I have ever seen. Aeons of grinding seas have left polished near-spheres and ovals, brown and red and black, and blue and grey and striped, shapes that are a joy to gaze on, or even to caress in the hand.

The sculptor Barbara Hepworth was once asked what she meant by the beautiful curved shapes she created in wood and stone. She answered, *"I'm trying to create, in a few hours with a chisel, what the sea and waves take a million years to create."*

Beautiful shapes, untouched by chisel, are all around us. A wave itself, curving towards a beach – or the plume of spray that comes slowly up and falls back on a stormy day at Blackhead.

And textures too – like the Dublin hills when sun follows rain, and you know how they would feel if you could reach out and run your hand over them. Or a ploughed field on the side of a hill, a square of brown corduroy stitched into a green patchwork quilt. Or the metallic gleam of the sod itself as it comes away from the ploughshare.

Have you ever looked at a stand of beech trees in winter? Against the sky the tops of the bare branches all line up together, as if some Cyclops with a giant shears had clipped them.

In his poem, Rupert Brooke remembers, *"Wet roof beneath the lamplight, and the strong crust of friendly bread . . . Rainbows and the blue-bitter smoke of wood . . . These I have loved,"* he says. And so have I.

Lord, that I may see.

4

ON a warm afternoon lately I strolled past a buddleia tree
outside a lonely bungalow in east Clare. When I looked
again, I realised the tree was alive with butterflies.

I counted five different species. One Red Admiral was so drunk
with nectar that I got within a couple of inches of him and could
watch the proboscis, like a tiny elephant's trunk, probing the
riches of each blossom. An hour later, as I turned to walk away,
I was amazed at the feeling of peace that had come upon me. I
find wild creatures do that to me – as though they revive in me
that sense of awe that I had as a child.

Once as I walked by the Shannon, a heron lurched lazily into
the air, flapped about 50 yards and landed again. When I
reached him, he did the same thing again. And again, every
time I caught up with him. Then he disappeared. I looked and
I looked, and suddenly I saw him standing in the reeds just
below me, silent and still. He was only feet away. I too stayed
silent and unmoving.

We kept our mutual vigil for maybe half an hour. Finally he
flapped lazily out over the river. When I walked on, I was filled
with wonder and peace.

I went back to that butterfly tree again another day, and this
time I saw the young woman of the house and I asked her had
she noticed the butterflies. She hadn't. When she saw them she
called her children, and my last sight as I walked away was of
a family entranced.

Lord, that I may see.

5

WHEN did you last look at your hands? I don't mean see them – we see them every day as they serve our needs. But *look* at them. I mean tracing those extraordinary lines etched into the palm before we were born, or following the veins on the back of the hand, or counting the hairs on the back of each finger.

When did you last examine those minute ridges that make you unique – the ridges we call fingerprints? Can you remember what yours are like? Are they oval or circular, or are they tiny gothic arches with flying buttresses? And how do yours differ from one finger to another?

I know people who couldn't answer that, because they haven't really truly looked at their fingers since childhood.

The same is true of all our body. The only thing we truly possess is our own body, and it happens to be the most stupendous creation in the universe. But how many of us have ever looked with awe and wonder on the quite incredible organism that is our body – an organism that functions without a single wheel; that moves on two feet without tottering; that navigates by light and communicates by the air; that can reproduce itself; and, above all, that is able to become aware of itself?

And the first step in that awareness is surely to look at oneself. First with wonder. Then with awe. Then with love. And then with gratitude.

Lord, that I may see.

MARY RIEKE MURPHY

1

ONCE a month I go to the grocery to stock up. Plastic car-
tons, squeeze bottles, boxes and tins brim over the giant
trolley that's almost too heavy to push. It's a chore. It gives me
attitude.

The one saving grace is that I have the store off by heart. I can
shop without thinking. Until last month. It had been refur-
bished.

The rows of shelves were shorter so there were more corners to
turn. They were set skew-wise, so left and right didn't make
sense. And stock wasn't where it was supposed to be. I had to
stop, stand still in the aisles to picture the shelves at home to see
what I needed.

By the time I got to the checkouts I was ready to implode. Until
I spotted the one checkout with a woman helping to pack. It
was just about free.

I pulled up, emptied as much as I could onto the conveyer belt
and waited. And waited some more. The woman at the
checkout, the woman sacking and the customer were talking.
So I piled more groceries, hoping to be patient and to be noticed.
I wasn't patient or noticed.

Next thing the woman at the till got off her stool and left. She
walked all the way across to talk to a manageress. With so
many groceries unpacked it was too late for me to back out. I
had no choice but to stand and bear it. Which became even
more exasperating when, on her way back to the stool, the woman
stopped, not at one but two checkouts. She was looking for a
biro to borrow.

Finally back in her place, regardless of me, she and her cronies started talking all over again. Their heads came together now over a docket.

I got a few urges – scream, complain, say something sarcastic or ... but then she saw me. Raising her head in a laugh the checkout woman looked my way.

"Sorry, love. Won't be a minute." She winked.

I watched and saw now, not three inefficient women but three happy faces.

They reminded me of years ago and the local shop. What passed across its counter was not a mountain of groceries but heaps of conversation, advice and friendship.

2

THE bus was almost full when I got on in town. The man shifted his travel bag under the seat to make room. After a quick hello, he asked me if I knew where a certain drug and alcohol rehabilitation centre was, a residential one.

"The stop before mine, almost at the end of the route," I said. *"I'll let you know in plenty of time."* We couldn't see out. The windows were fogged and running with condensation. If you wiped them you'd only get wet. So we fell into conversation.

He was from the country, had come to Dublin by train that morning, a three-hour journey. He knew his way around the city centre but had to ask what bus to catch for the rehab centre. He had been born and lived in the same townland all his life and would not like the city, even though winter was coming on harsh in the country. Storms and floods and gale-force winds. *"The electricity went again this year. But we had it for Christmas. It didn't go till Stephen's Day. You'd only notice at night."*

There was nothing remarkable about the man except his acceptance; not complaining about the ESB, not worrying about the time spent travelling that morning.

"I'm going back tonight."

"Will you get home late?" I asked.

"It'll be after 10 before we get there." He pointed his thumb over his shoulder to the back of the bus. *"My family's with me."*

The bus had emptied when we got near his stop. His family came up front – a woman his age, two small children and a baby asleep in a younger woman's arms. They sat patiently.

The bus rounded the corner and I pointed the way to the centre. As they walked towards it, I remembered what day it was. 8 January. Two days after the Magi travelled to see a newborn child. This family was making a long journey too, to see someone belonging to them struggling to be reborn.

3

MY mom is a bottom-line woman. Her favourite expression is, *"A fish never got caught with its mouth closed."* Ask a question, you get an answer and then she moves on to the next activity. She's a doer and being 81 does not stop her.

Ruth is 89 and lives three doors up the street. Mom goes to see her every Monday morning. Ruth's a talker. Starts the minute she opens the door. Before you know it you're sitting on the end of the couch, Ruth's at the other. She's perched sideways so she can see out the long front window. Last time I was home, Ruth was keeping an eye on the house across the street. A woman in her forties, never married, owns it. A man was painting the outside. Ruth found out he's single. *"Why, it took him all last week just to finish those gutters. I think he's going slow. And on purpose, too. I hope so, don't you? They both need somebody, don't you think?"*

Ruth watches Mom answer. Ruth's hearing is weak. And she has heart trouble. She wears a small gadget. In an emergency she can press it and it rings Mom's phone. It has happened about five times – three by accident when Ruth turned over on to it in her sleep. *"Pitch dark, middle of the night, I went. It scared me,"* Mom said. *"But we get a good laugh out of it, don't we?"* They both laughed then.

Later I asked Mom, outright. *"Are you afraid of dying?"*

"Not afraid," she looked up from her crossword, *"I just don't want to."* And that was that.

Another morning we drove up the street. I was at the wheel. It's the only thing Mom let's me do for her. *"There's Ruth. Stop, will you?"* Ruth came to Mom's open window. She put her hands on the ledge.

"Your hands, Ruth," Mom patted them, *"they're so cold."*

"'Course they are, kid. Didn't you know? I'm already dead . . . just too cantankerous to lie down." They laughed. The Reaper doesn't look so grim when I'm with them.

4

THE first time I planted daffodils, our baby was napping so I took my time. I placed the bulbs just so along the wall, dug the holes exactly as deep as the trowel, gave each bulb a right twist into place and crumbled the soil before showering it back into the holes. I planted the daffs in threesomes to create a cluster, to get the magazine look.

When they bloomed I guarded them ferociously. I fenced them against the March winds, chased cats and dogs and reminded children who sat on the low wall swinging their legs not to kick them. I picked only a judicious few for the dinner table. They made a wonderful show.

Next time I planted daffodils was eight years later when we moved house. We had three children by then – active, omnipresent. They didn't take naps. Most anything I did, they did too.

Time slipped away. It was too late to get to the garden centre to select from choice bulbs so I settled for a handi-pak at the grocery. The minute I started pulling at the mesh bag to get them open, bickering broke out. Who got first go, who'd give out the bulbs, who got to use the trowel, who'd say where to plant them? The squabbling put me tugging so hard, the bag ripped. The bulbs flipped, dropped and rolled.

After a mad scramble we got them into a big bowl and went outside. I picked out one bulb, showed the kids how to tell top from bottom and then stood with my back to the garden and tossed the bulbs over my shoulder. *"Plant them where they landed, as deep as the spoon,"* I said and handed a sharp-edged serving spoon to each. They set to.

In spring the daffs appeared all helter skelter, open to the wind and in the way of mowing the grass. Until the birthday. I found the daffs, every single one, jammed into jamjars on the table.

But I didn't mind. Motherhood loosens you up.

Besides, on a window ledge too high for little arms, my pot of daffodils stood safe, their heads bent, watching.

5

WHEN Bus Átha Cliath quit giving change, I made sure I had the exact fare. But one day I stepped onto the bus and there he was. *"What?"* I asked. *"I'm the only one left,"* the conductor said and stepped back to let me pass.

A woman got on. She held one child's hand, carried a younger. She sat opposite me on seats that face each other. She put the children sitting across from her, the smaller safe by the window. The little one was restless. She pulled off her mittens and dropped them on the floor. Her mother picked them up. She pulled off her hat. Mother took it straight away. *"Sit still."* The mother pointed a warning finger. Her voice was loud, almost rough. She sat back. Her tired eyes closed. The little one amused herself. She flopped her feet in and out, in and out. Then she ran the zip on her jacket up and down, down and up. Next she squirmed onto her knees, stood up on the seat and pressed both hands against the window to steady herself. Something outside excited her. She started slapping the window. Mam's eyes shot open. She went for the child. Caught her round the tummy. Whisked her off her feet. Jammed her back in place. *"Don't let me catch you standing up again. Hear me?"* Her voice was harsh; she'd got a fright. She gave the child a right smack on the legs.

Two women in front of me hadn't quit talking the entire journey. Until now. Their heads turned as one. They watched the mother. She wasn't able for their staring. She frowned at the child, who was wailing. She frowned at her hands, strong, red, in her lap. She scowled out the window. The bigger child put her arms around the little one. The two women kept watching. The conductor came back, stood between the watching women and the mother.

"Oh my ears!" He cupped them and jiggled his head, clowning. The little one stopped crying. *"Next thing she'd be down on the floor,"* the mother explained herself. *"You can't be up to them,"* he said and rested his hip against the seat awhile. By the time he moved on the two little ones and their mother were talking, happy. The conductor had stood by them.

JOHN W SEXTON

1

ON the street in north London where we lived in the 1960s, everybody knew that you simply didn't argue with those Turkish boys.

But the three Turkish boys, and even their cantankerous grandfather, were nothing, absolutely nothing compared to their younger sister. At only 10 years of age, it was generally agreed that she was dangerous. People openly said that she was mad. When you saw her in the street it was always best to simply keep out of the way.

One Sunday my father bought me a wooden glider at the fair. When I got home I put it together and took it out into the street. On its maiden voyage it soared upwards in a beautiful sweep that took it over the houses and nearly into the next street. All the kids looked up in amazement as it came down to land. Unfortunately, it landed outside the house of the Turkish family, right in front of the youngest daughter. She was sitting in the middle of the pavement and by the time I got to her she had the glider in her lap.

I had never stood that close to her before. Her eyes shone with what I could only imagine was madness. Then, giggling as she did it, she snapped my glider into tiny pieces. I stood there, stunned, and her eyes flashed with otherworldly arrogance. And in that instant I hated her. It was the first pure hatred that I had ever felt.

That was over 30 years ago, but I can still see her eyes today. I see her eyes each time I look into the face of my autistic son. Looking into his eyes I am looking into hers. And it is only now that I understand what she was trying to communicate.

She was daring me. She was daring me to hate. She was daring me to understand. She was daring me to love.

2

ON Christmas Eve I had been roped in at the last minute to drive to town for some shopping. As a result I missed Santa, who had made his appearance while I was away. Through barely contained excitement, my youngest son told me how they had come into the living room to investigate a tremendous racket of banging and coughing, only to find Santa pushing back a potted plant that had been blocking the fireplace. I was told how they gave him a great hug, his belly as soft as a pillow, his beard nearly touching his belt.

"Santa told me it took 500 years to grow, Dad."

"Oh, I'm sorry I missed him, I'm really disappointed."

"Yes, and he said that he was able to get down the chimney because he had drunk some 'elasticated soup', and it made his body like rubber. And he had these black, shiny boots with laces, and he said they were fireproof, waterproof and spaceproof."

Luckily, Mammy had had the presence of mind to capture some of this on video. Later that night we watched it together.

"Please turn off the lights," pleaded Santa, *"I am only used to the light of the stars."*

The main light was switched off and, in the murky light of the Christmas tree, Santa seemed far happier. I noticed that he kept looking over the heads of our sons and into the large mantelpiece mirror. He was looking at himself, as if he feared that at any moment he might fall to pieces. Then he turned and looked directly into the camera, and I found myself staring straight into his eyes.

While the children were opening their presents he simply disappeared. It was not long afterwards that I returned home. And I knew it would be a full year before he would come back into our lives.

3

WHEN I was six I followed the adventures of old Father Cummings, the parish priest at St John Vianni's Church. He didn't appear in the cinema, but used to do live shows at mass every Sunday. For most of the week he just looked like an old man with grey skin who dressed in black. But on Sundays he would be transformed, dressed in vestments the colour of blood or the colour of bruises.

As he stood on the altar, the light would shine on him from the stained-glass windows, and the pictures from the windows would play across his body. Depending on where he stood, the faces from the windows would slip onto his, so that sometimes he'd have the face of Jesus, sometimes the face of John the Baptist, and sometimes the face of the Virgin Mary. When he lifted up the chalice, it would place a reflection on his forehead like a golden egg. I noticed that all the adults would go up to him and he'd place pieces of white paper into their mouths. Piece of paper after piece of paper would come out of the chalice, but it would never be empty. Through some process I didn't understand, the pieces of paper got turned into bread. Then when they got into your mouth they became the skin of Jesus.

By the time I was nine I had already got to eat those pieces of paper, but they never tasted like skin. By that time I was reading *The Adventures of the Green Lantern*. The Green Lantern had a magic ring that was far more powerful than Father Cummings' chalice, and the Green Lantern could breathe in outer space or beneath the sea. He fought with creatures that could eat mountains or swallow oceans, and he never lost. Unfortunately, unlike Father Cummings, he never appeared at mass on Sundays.

4

DURING the recent cold weather we had a visitor. He was quite strange, to say the least. He was made entirely of snow and refused to come in from the garden, and at night he slept standing up. To say that he came from somewhere would not be entirely correct, but to say that he came from nothing wouldn't be right either. The truth is, we made him ourselves, or at least we thought we had.

His name was Mr Noman and, to be perfectly honest, I hadn't realised how well travelled he was, thinking all the time that he was confined to the colder climates.

"Oh no," said Mr Noman. *"I only look like this when it snows. In the summer my body is a shaft of light, and thank you very much by the way for giving me a loan of this nose. Most people give me lumps of coal, which quite frankly play havoc with my sinuses, or else sticks or carrots. Carrots are better than sticks any day of the week, but the best nose of all is a tangerine. So thank you very much for this tangerine. For through it I can smell the scent of summer groves, and my sinuses are as clear as a bell."*

During the night, Mr Noman tried to do a backwards somersault in his sleep, and the following morning we found him broken in half. Furthermore, some little birdies had split his tangerine nose and eaten out all the insides, so all he had left was a strip of peeling. Instead of two good solid stones for eyes, all he had now were two tiny dead leaves, with a blade of grass for his mouth. When he spoke, we could hardly hear a word he said. On that second night he left with the rain.

Snow is a little like childhood. When it's there its presence seems strangely transcendent and at the same time dazzlingly real. And then it's gone.

5

THIRTEEN years ago my brother Gerard died as the result of a car accident. He was an 18-year-old passenger and was driven through the window of a launderette. For two and a half months he lay in a coma, until, finally, his heart stopped.

I had been away from home, married, for some time, and was shocked how this small boy had grown, become a man, and had got himself killed. I can't think of him in that car, can't imagine how he got there. All I can think of is a young boy playing in the garden with his football. He trips over a stone and falls headlong into the flower-bed. As he tumbles forward, his fall seems to go on for a long time, as if he has fallen completely off the edge of the world. But then he lands brutally amongst sharp stones, only to find that he has shrunk to the size of a drawing pin.

He rises to his feet, but the turbulence from the wings of a fluttering butterfly casts him once more into the air. He falls against grass as thick as sheets, the weight from his body triggering the mechanism of a dandelion, the seeds of which explode into fluffy kites. He watches their spoke-like shadows race fleetingly over the ground.

But his observation is dizzily interrupted as he is swept up into the slimy skirt of a passing snail. As he is drawn into the thick, suffocating jelly of the snail's wake, he thinks briefly of his football. It lies somewhere in the tumultuous chaos of the garden, waiting to be kicked.

JOHN SEYMOUR

1

PEOPLE have given names to the various ages through which humans have passed in our history. There is the Stone Age, the Iron Age and the Age of Reason, for example. Many people have tried to name the age in which we now live. The Age of Waste is a good one, for undoubtedly we create more rubbish than any previous generation. The Age of Greed is another runner. But, personally, I name this age the Age of Plunder, for this earth is being plundered as never before. The forests of the world are being cut down at frightening speed. Wherever there are fish in the sea there are men in huge floating destroyers trying to get them out. All of them – not just enough. There seems to be no such thing as enough. The whalers won't be satisfied until they kill the last whale – the ivory hunters the last elephant. There must be nothing left for future generations to make use of. The greed of agriculturalists is destroying the soil all about the globe. The last drop of oil – and natural gas – must be squeezed from the earth now, as soon as can be. No moderation can ever be observed.

Of course it cannot go on; either a new age must replace this one or we come to the end of the human story – and it will serve us jolly well right!

Well, the name I propose for the new age that we must all work for is the Age of Healing. And nothing less can save our planet now.

2

WHEN God gave man dominion over the birds of the air and the beasts of the field, He did not intend that man should abuse this power and act like a tyrant and a wanton destroyer. I submit that He meant that we should exercise our dominion with humanity and humility – acting, as it were, as the Viceroy of God – not the king himself and lord and master.

Now, over the centuries of evolution, the life force has produced many strange and wonderful things. Our intelligence is simply another experiment of the life force. If it serves the purpose of the life force, it will survive and we will flourish. If it works against that purpose, it will simply cease to exist as many another experiment has done in the past.

We are not here for our own sake alone – we are here to serve all life on this planet. We have a right, indeed a duty, to regulate and control but not to usurp the role of our true master and king. To start interfering with the building blocks of life – to mess about with genes and DNA so as to create new species just for profit – is definitely to usurp the role of the Creator and is to invite retribution. To treat our fellow creatures with cruelty – just because we are more intelligent – is not what is intended by the Almighty.

Viceroys throughout history have often been tempted to usurp the role of the king, and it has never paid them. Look what happened to Mark Anthony.

3

FOR the most of history, humankind believed we were not a part of nature but were created quite separately and independently from it. Paradoxically, while people believed this they behaved as if they *were* part of nature, for they acted with humanity and compassion towards the other living creatures.

Then along came Darwin and convinced most people that we *are* part of nature. Just another animal and descended from apes. Paradoxically again, we have behaved as though we are not part of nature but that the animals and plants are simply there for us to exploit and, if we want to, exterminate. Now I call this belief my 'ultimate heresy' and have written a book about it. For it is my belief that, every time we destroy a species, a habitat or a life form, we are actually destroying part of ourselves. If we persist in this – it will ultimately bring about *our* extermination. If we continue to act as though we are the lords and masters of the universe, which has simply been put there for our benefit, we will continue to pervert and destroy it and ultimately destroy ourselves. The Creator has given us intelligence and dexterity and these things set us apart from other animals, but they do not give us the right to control nature just for our own purposes. A wise gardener or farmer knows he has to work with nature rather than conducting some sort of fight against the living world. This art of stewardship is one we would be wise to discover.

4

THE 'merchants of greed' who run our planet today call any-one trying to curb their nefarious activities a 'Luddite'. They use this as an insult – I look on it as a great compliment.

I am old enough to remember the earth as it was before most of the wonders of modern science were invented. There were vir-tually no aeroplanes, and country people used to say, *"If God had meant us to fly he'd have given us wings."* Well we have them now. And what do they do? They pollute the earth's atmos-phere; they destroy the ozone layer, which protects us from can-cer; they use up the earth's limited store of fossil fuel; they make a fiendish noise and, well, they carry thousands of people to foreign countries which they proceed to try and turn into the same boring place that they have come from. And of course they drop bombs on people.

And tractors – they caused the death of rural communities as they made the rural population unemployable – it took them 20 years to run the Great Western Plains of the United States into the Dust Bowl. And they do the same now in India and in Africa.

And what about cars? They poison the air in our cities and are a chief cause of climate change. When I was a kid, if you wanted to go to the nearest market town you went in the 'carrier's wagon'. It cost you sixpence and it was great fun.

Yes, I am a Luddite and very proud to be one, too.

5

WHEN I was a boy I lived in an enormous country house in England. My father was rich and employed many servants. Life was anything but simple – there were too many servants, too much ceremony and too many regulations.

But sometimes it suited my parents to pack me off with my beloved Nanny to spend a holiday with *her* family.

My Nanny's daddy was head horseman of a big farm. He and his largish family lived in a small cottage down beside a little backwater. Old Mr Fisher had to get up at five every morning to 'bait' (that is, feed) his horses, and groom them, and plait their tails and manes and get them ready for a hard day's ploughing. He used to lift me up on the back of one to ride out to the field. Life in the cottage was nothing if not simple. There was no electricity – we had oil lamps and candles. No running water. No radio, and television had not been invented. There was a simple coal-burning cooking stove and Mrs Fisher used to cook the most delicious food I have ever eaten, before or since. Once a week I was bathed with the whole family looking on. There was a feeling of mutual love and respect in the family that I will never forget. And it taught me to value the simple things in life.

Simplicity is the key to holiness and happiness – of that I have been ever since convinced.

EAMONN SWEENEY

1

ONE of the most familiar sights of summer remains for me one of the most resonant. As I walked through Cork city recently, they seemed to be everywhere. Young girls and boys in Communion outfits. The city and the country might have changed but the outfits could have come from 50 years ago. It was noticeable, too, that on this occasion the kids would be dressed far more expensively than the adults with them. Some people had made every possible effort to get their children dressed up for the big day.

Perhaps the best fictional representation of this struggle is in Ken Loach's great film *Raining Stones*. A man brings himself to the brink of personal disaster due to his efforts to buy a Communion outfit for his daughter. The interesting thing about this film by Loach, a left-wing director not noted for his sympathy to religion, is that finally the proud father's struggle is shown to have been worthwhile. His instinct that his daughter needed to be made special on this particular day is borne out.

That is why a Communion day still has such power and enchantment. People sometimes observe that the secularisation of our society has cost us a sense of ritual and mystery. Often this is just a platitude. But, looking at dozens of seven-year-olds crossing the Lee, proud parents in tow, it's impossible to avoid the conclusion that there was something which went beyond cold logic and rationalism. Something it would be sad to lose.

2

L IMERICK gets a bad press. So does Beirut but at least that is, to some degree, justified. Munster's second city on the other hand seems to inspire a quite irrational disdain among otherwise collected people. It's a pity, because it's quite a pleasant place and does contain Ireland's most remarkable museum.

The Hunt Museum reminds you of what museums were like in their infancy. Before careful classification, contextualisation, cabinetisation, the museum was a collection of curiosities designed to evoke wonder in the spectator. The qualification for inclusion was simply that the object must be interesting to look at. The Hunt Museum of course is not *that* unstructured, but its disparate collection of objects from all over the world often seems to have as much to do with wonder as with scientific knowledge. It's striking how much of the collection is inspired by religious belief. The chalices, wooden statues, rosary beads and altar paintings are very different in style. Grand works of Italian neo-classical mastery, rubbing shoulders with wooden statues from 14th-century Germany. And simply beautiful rosary beads from Penal Law Ireland. The story they tell is of awe-inspiring faith. In the shadow of the Black Death, the Central European Middle Ages produced religious art of a profound, calm and controlled nature. Whatever your beliefs, to regard these in the Hunt Museum is to have a link with something way beyond normal experience.

3

WHAT is Europe's most popular destination for Catholic pilgrims? If you guessed Lourdes you're wrong. It has been surpassed by San Giovanni Rotondo, which receives over 6 million visitors a year. San Giovanni Rotondo is the burial place of the man who was born Francesco Forgione but is now known as Padre Pio.

Padre Pio was beatified this May after a long campaign on his behalf by many devotees, both lay and religious. The campaign needed to be particularly intense because his relationship with the hierarchy of the Catholic Church in Rome was not a happy one. At one point, they attempted to transfer him to Spain and senior churchmen were constantly sceptical about the stigmata which appeared on his hands as well as the stories of bilocation, cures and visions which surrounded him. Yet, he now inspires a devotion, perhaps only surpassed by that to Our Lady.

Why has this come about in the face of such opposition from the organised Church? The Vatican correspondent for *La Stampa*, Marco Tassati, commented that Padre Pio seems to belong to older times, and an older faith. Perhaps this is one of the reasons he attracts such devotion. Near San Giovanni Rotondo is the village of Monte San Angelo. A thousand years ago it was a place of famous pilgrimage and in AD999 the holy Roman emperor, Otto the Third, visited to pray that the prophesied millennial apocalypse would not happen. How much has faith and human nature changed in the thousand years since?

4

WE are a society obsessed with anniversaries. It's not just centenaries which are celebrated these days – 35th, 45th, and 60th anniversaries, even 50th and 10th, prompt stock-taking and nostalgic looks back. Usually these celebrations are connected with an attempt to impose narrative logic on the happenings involved; an effort to pin an exact meaning on the Easter Rising, the Second World War or the Great Hunger. How will we mark the 20th anniversary of the papal visit this September? Will there be any agreement on what is fitting? At the time, such a question would have seemed ridiculous. An abiding memory of the time was the sense of national unity and excitement. The number of people who saw Pope John Paul II was phenomenal for such a small country. Reaction to his visit was almost uniformly positive. The media coverage verged on the reverential.

It seems a very different country now. It's unlikely that a straw poll taken anywhere would elicit unanimous agreement that the visit had a beneficial effect. I remember going to mass in Galway. It was an extraordinarily moving experience at the time for me and for many people. But how do we regard it now? It's a question worth asking in September. People's reactions may be far more complex than blanket acceptance or rejection of that week when the nation seemed to stand still. On the verge of what exactly?

5

I WAS born and raised a Catholic. I am no longer one, primarily because I have lost faith. Murray Kempton, a great American journalist and a devoutly religious man, said that those who are *"born without innocence"* are doomed to live in a *"secular hell"*. Perhaps a similar fate awaits those who lose their innocence. There are a great many people who find no joy in the fact that they are no longer able to believe. The loss of faith can be as debilitating for some as it is liberating for others. The phrase 'post-Catholic' gets bandied about a lot in contemporary Ireland and is, to my mind, misused. It is most commonly taken to denote a gleeful secular society where religion no longer matters to people. But, just as the phrase 'post-war' means that the war remains a defining quality of a society, so, in a 'post-Catholic' country, Catholicism is an integral part of the present as much as of the past.

I think most people of my generation were profoundly affected by our given religion. And I am grateful for the sense of belonging it gave me as a child; for the community spirit engendered by Sunday mass; for the ritual seriousness of my First Communion and Confirmation; for the excitement of stories from the Gospel; for the thrill I felt as an 11-year-old seeing the Pope in Galway; for the sheer childish joy of a visit to Knock; for nurturing the idea that belief is something to be taken seriously even after you have rejected it. As Mary Kenny's excellent *Goodbye to Catholic Ireland* points out, the Church has taken a much-deserved battering recently, but to deny its influence is to trivialise ourselves.

COLM TÓIBÍN

1

ARCHITECTURE is an arrangement of light. If they knocked down Enniscorthy Cathedral, I could build it from memory as it was in 1965 or 1966. I remember the crowd at 12 o'clock mass, the brave ones walking up the centre aisle looking for seats – stiletto heels, maxi coats, all the new style – and others more timid, who arrived early or moved warily up the side aisles looking for a seat at Calvary or Our Lady's Altar. There were lilies on the altar and everything was golden and shiny; there was an opulence in the arches and columns, the cut stone, the sheer height and vastness. There was nothing else like it in our world.

One Sunday morning when I was an altar boy, I was serving eight o'clock mass and I went to ring the '20 to' bell with Ned Earle, who was the sacristan. We crossed from the vestry to the main altar, genuflecting as we passed the tabernacle, and then over by Calvary where there was a small door painted that watery, grainy brown that you get in institutions. Ned Earle had the big old key with him and, when he opened the door, we walked up the winding stone steps to the belfry. Ringing the bell required skill. You had to tug hard at the rope, but not yank it, everything firm and stable, nothing sudden and uncontrolled. And when we finished we stood out on the small platform and looked down over the town towards the Slaney. Ned Earle said nothing for a while. I wondered what he was doing standing there. He was a practical man. He liked being busy. I waited beside him and said nothing. *"Look down there,"* he said. *"Look at the white mist."* Down beyond St Senan's, hovering over the river, was a dense white mist that could have been smoke. *"I've stood here every day,"* he said, *"for 40 years and I've never seen that before, I've never seen mist before, that colour, in all the years."* He stood looking at it, as though he wanted to be sure he would remember it. He shook his head at the newness of it, and then we both walked back down the stone steps towards the body of the cathedral.

2

IN 1993, the Wexford Opera Festival put on three plays by
Billy Roche in the Theatre Royal in Wexford. I remember the
fierce cold clarity of the winter light on the quays as I walked the
town that Saturday and Sunday. For the three nights the theatre was packed with local people. The plays are hard – there is
a rawness in the emotional world of Billy Roche. A searing sort
of honesty. He writes better than anyone about what weakness
is like, how weak we all are. His Wexford is a melancholy
place, and there were moments in his trilogy, for example when
Danger Doyle opened the door of the bookie shop in *Poor Beast
in the Rain*, when the whole theatre, a whole community, held
its breath and you realised that this is what theatre is for –
enacting in public our most private fears and secrets.

On the Sunday night after the final play, there was a small party
for the cast and the Roche family and friends, and others who
had stayed behind. And I saw something that night which I did
not think would be possible in my lifetime in Ireland. I was
brought up in a world where writers were run out of places,
where books were banned and even burnt, where writers went
to London, or America, or kept apart, or drank themselves to
death. That night I watched the Roches, Billy's mother and
father, his wife, his daughter, all of them keeping close to him,
smiling, laughing, having a drink, and then there was some
great singing and it was a late night.

For them, I think, it was almost ordinary. There was nothing
special or self-conscious in the way they related to the man who
had put his whole world on the stage, taken the private and the
personal and transformed it into riveting drama, but I couldn't
take my eyes off them that night. It was the first intimation I had
that we were slowly starting to live in a new sort of country.

3

IT was Galway in the early 1990s and there was a rumour going around that something special was going to happen in the Druid Theatre at lunchtime. That small space had taken on for me and for many others a special intensity. It was where some of the best new plays and productions had been acted out over the previous 10 years. But this event at lunchtime was different, it would be just two fiddlers from the Tulla Ceilí Band on the stage of the Druid, but I was told to go to it, it would be worth it. The men were in their sixties, dressed in suits and collars and ties. Their bearing was formal. They sat and played for us and the playing was beautiful. In Irish dance music you wait for the end of each line, like it was a poem or a wave of the sea, and then the next line comes with its repetition or its variation. There is a peculiar aura of inevitability and acceptance in this music. The notes are like seasons. Listening gets you used to the idea that time will pass and things will move on and be replaced.

Half-way through the concert in the Druid, two more players came on – the fiddler Martin Hayes and Dennis Cahill on guitar. And as the four men began to play I realised that one of the men in suits was Martin Hayes' father. Martin Hayes had long hair and, like his companion, was dressed casually. This might have been a site of some conflict, not only sartorial, but between generations and musical tastes. Instead, it was a picture of pure harmony and sweetness. The older men's style was serious and straightforward. Martin Hayes was emphasising the gorgeousness of the music, he was letting it soar, but he too could be as rigid and technically perfect as the older men when he wanted to be. We watched them, then, utterly content, making way for each other, suddenly coming back together, smiling and then letting the music lift for us, pure delight.

4

IN Crossmaglen and Cullyhanna and Forkhill and all the villages around, people were watchful. Careful. It was south Armagh in 1985, a territory portrayed as bandit country by the tabloid press. There was, we were told, a war going on between the British Army and the IRA – and sometimes you saw signs of that in graffiti, in the Army helicopters coming and going, in the checkpoints and the Army presence in the square in Crossmaglen. But most of the time it was quiet, it had the calmness of any country area in Ireland, and you were never sure whether the term 'bandit country' was deceptive or whether the calm was deceptive. In the end I discovered that maybe everything was deceptive.

That September in Forkhill, there was a singing festival – it happens each year – and that too could be deceptive if you arrived thinking that it would tell you something about Republican politics in south Armagh. The singing festival in Forkhill was about singing, and the songs were about love and landscape, memory and loss. People were interested in the quality of the voices, the grace notes and flourishes, a verse added or left out, the other version of a song. And that night I heard something that is with me still in all its glory, that I will never forget. I had heard Maighread Ní Dhomhnaill's voice on an LP by Skara Brae in the early 1970s, but now out of the blue in a pub in Forkhill that Saturday night she sang "Roisín Dubh". Everything stopped. The cash register didn't make a sound; there wasn't the slightest whisper. Her voice has astonishing power and control; and there is a range of feeling and expression and sweetness in what she does that took our breath away that night. This was, for me, a new sort of south Armagh in which the music soared above the issues of the day and made me wonder if I should go on being a journalist or try my hand at writing something closer to the music I had heard.

5

IN Velasquez's painting *The Waterseller* there are three figures – an old weather-beaten man in a ragged tunic (he is the
waterseller); then there is a boy to whom he hands a glass of
water with a fig in it; and finally there is a man in the background who is already drinking the water. Three objects – an
earthenware jug, a glazed vase and the glass tumbler – play just
as important a role in the painting as the three figures. There is
no obvious drama, no one is speaking or struggling – instead,
there is a curious stillness in the picture. It plays with textures
and surfaces – the glazed beside the unglazed, the bright white
sleeve of the old man's shirt against the flat brown of his tunic,
his sunburnt skin against the soft skin of the boy.

Towards the bottom of the painting there are drops of water on
the front of the earthenware jug and signs of water dripping.
These are painted with astonishing skill. They have a beautiful
randomness about them, but they must have been carefully
planned and worked onto the canvas with immense dexterity
and cunning. But I do not think that is the reason why they are
so touching, why they make the scene seem so vulnerable. I am
looking now at the drop of water that is still moving between
the drips made by other drops of water which have already
rolled down the side of the jar. This drop of water is shaped like
a tear, but it does not remind me of a tear, it is only a drop of
water, it stands for nothing except itself. Yet it is being asked to
carry a great deal of emotion in the painting, an emotion that is
spectacularly missing in the relationship between the three figures. It knows nothing about grief or age, it sparkles in the light.
I love its glorious indifference, its pure freedom and fluidity.
The part of me that thinks will insist that these drops of water
are merely there to establish verisimilitude – the painter im-
pressing us with his skill. But the other part of me that takes in
sensations and knows only how to feel, picks up a blast of pure
emotion and brief respite from these brush strokes – not everything is fixed, they seem to say, not everything will return to
dust.

BRIAN TRENCH

1

I HEARD a radio presenter pull himself up the other day about using the phrase, *"I'm no Einstein"*.

"So, who was this Einstein anyway?" he asked. *"And what made him so special?"*

When we want to indicate that something is particularly difficult we may refer to it as 'rocket science'. When we want to refer to someone as particularly brilliant we may refer to them as an Einstein. In this way, science and scientists are marked out as distant, unattainable, even alien. But this week – Science Week Ireland – scientific institutions and individual scientists, as well as those with an active, though non-professional, interest in science, will be attempting to demonstrate that it need not be this way.

It is a cliché, but an unavoidable reality all the same, that science is more and more part of the fabric of our everyday lives and we are more and more affected by it. Yet most of us are barely aware of the scope of its influence and very few of us can use the language of science with any confidence. There may be a very good reason why we cannot grasp the detail of science. For a start, it is communicated in highly specialised forms. So, we may conclude that it is better to leave the scientists to get on with science while we get on with whatever we're good at. We no longer allow this for politics, education, religion, or much else. It is a mark of our growing maturity and sense of responsibility as citizens that we demand to hold leaders and experts to account. Politics is too important to be left to politicians, we say. Science may now be too important to be left to scientists.

2

WE hear fairly frequently about new techniques in cloning, *in vitro* fertilisation and genetic manipulation. From the scientist's perspective these are distinct developments, each one involving quite different methods. Some have great promise of medical advances, others may have a less certain application. From the perspective of many outside science, however, the news of these developments accumulates into an awareness that something very significant is going on in the biological and medical sciences. And, for some, the awareness becomes concern, unease, suspicion, or even a feeling of being threatened. Then scientists are accused of 'playing God' or 'interfering with nature'. *"Leave religion out of it,"* the scientists say, *"let's talk about the science."* But what this response misses is how completely science is enmeshed with religion and with politics and commerce.

Last June, the announcement was made that a working draft of the human genome – a sketch map of the arrangement of humans' genetic material – had been completed. The announcement of this major scientific and technical achievement was orchestrated by the US President and the British Prime Minister. It involved a hastily negotiated compromise between private- and public-sector interests involved in the endeavour. The achievement was described by the US President as *"learning the language of God"*. I have had the good fortune to hear one of the leading researchers on the Human Genome Project, Dr John Sulston, speak about this work. He does so in a balanced, careful and considered manner. And he acknowledges that politics, finance and morality all enter the picture. Science is not divorced from social and political influences. Scientists cannot reasonably insist that the ethical issues arising from their work are not their concern. Developing the much-needed dialogue between science and society means recognising that pure science is not, in fact, pure.

3

CYCLING along a suburban road in Dublin recently, I passed a house with a plaque on its front wall stating that Erwin Schroedinger had lived there. Driving by, you might not even notice it. Over the last couple of years, quite a number of these plaques have been put up around Ireland, marking the birthplaces or workplaces of leading scientists and engineers. They recall a very considerable heritage of science and engineering which was for a long time largely hidden from view. Schroedinger, an Austrian, came to Ireland during World War II at the express invitation of Éamon de Valera. He worked at the Dublin Institute of Advanced Studies, and was later awarded the Nobel Prize for Physics. We have become so used to a view of ourselves as a people particularly gifted in literature and other imaginative arts that we tend to forget, or even dismiss, the notion that we could also be good at the cooler, more systematic disciplines of the sciences. We appear to have separated the arts and sciences more completely than elsewhere. We can offer only a few examples of the use of scientific ideas for creative expression – as in the very different cases of the novelists John Banville and Flann O'Brien, with his hilarious account of the supposed molecular theory. The day-to-day work in the lab can be dull and repetitive. Indeed, the mark of some work as specifically scientific may be in the constant repetition. It seems far removed from the passion and excitement of artistic endeavour. But there are moments of insight, inspiration, even excitement, in science too. I have heard scientists describe their work in passionate terms. Their appreciation of the subtlety and complexity of the materials they study is closely tied to an appreciation of beauty. We miss that in the way in which scientists present science to us.

4

MOST of us will never understand more than a tiny fraction of what constitutes science. But this does not mean that we can never engage with science meaningfully. At the very least we citizens, we non-scientists, should be able to ask questions of scientists – including the question, *"Why do you do this?"* The scientists should engage with those questions as fully as possible, and invite more. There need be no threat, nor any perception of threat, in such questions. To ensure our questions are better targeted, and to ensure we do not expect too much of science, we *do* need to learn how science is done.

Research is governed by many conditions – not least, resources. So when a researcher, or more usually a team of researchers, puts findings out, these are generally expressed in a way that makes it clear how and where, and under what circumstances, these findings are made. In other words, they may not be valid for all circumstances, or for all time. Before scientific findings are released, they are generally reviewed by people with knowledge of the field. They make judgements on how the findings relate to those already reported, and how well they follow from the assumptions of the research itself. These two aspects of the process are referred to as 'scientific method' and 'peer review', and scientists regard them as bywords for the reliability of published findings. On closer inspection, it can be seen that there are many varieties of scientific method and peer review, and few conform to the ideal.

PAOLO TULLIO

1

WHEN I spoke to my friends and told them that I'd be doing *A Living Word*, the reaction was nearly unanimous. *"Talk about food,"* they said. I suppose that's an understandable reaction – writing about food is perhaps my forte.

But being by birth an Italian, I've got a perspective that's different from many around me. And my attitude to food is equally idiosyncratic. There is, around the Mediterranean basin, a culture of food and hospitality that goes back for millennia. Sharing a meal is how people cemented relationships. A meal together turns a stranger into a friend. Breaking bread and sharing it is a concept deeply embedded into cultures all around the globe. Sharing food is the great binder, the unifier that brings people together.

Which is why, I suppose, family meals have traditionally been a feature of family life. The act of assembling and sharing a meal means that the whole family is together at the same time. It can often be the only time that all members are in the same place at the same time, and consequently it's an occasion when family matters can be discussed. Even the shared preparations and clearing away are all part of the family's group experience. Without its daily ritual there's a fear that somehow the family's cohesion would suffer.

So strongly do we feel this at a primal level, that all our major celebrations involve feasting. Even in the most secular houses, Christmas Day is centred on the feast. No wedding is complete without the guests assembling for a meal, many a business deal is concluded with a shared meal, and increasingly some wine as well.

Lastly, offering food is the hinge-point of hospitality. When we welcome people into our homes we reinforce the welcome with offers of food and drink. No matter how secular we've become, those Bible stories of feasts and sharing food still have echoes in our lives.

2

YESTERDAY I mentioned how hospitality is centred on food and drink. It's certainly the staple of hospitality, but it doesn't end there.

We have simple rules of etiquette in our society to help us keep a balance in our transactions with others. A simple example might be that we try not to arrive at a friend's house empty-handed. It's not that our hosts couldn't live without our offering, it's simply a recognition of the fact we're about to receive hospitality and our gift is a gesture towards balancing the books.

This balancing act between individuals is rarely spoken of directly, but nonetheless it governs much of what we do. No one can reasonably expect a *quid pro quo* for each and every deed – we allow the balance of give and take a fair bit of leeway. But when things get severely out of kilter, we not only notice, but, despite calling on our better nature, we also find feelings of resentment growing.

The reason for these feelings of resentment is simple. The individual who allows this transactional balance to tip away from the level is sending us a message that says, *"You are not my equal. Therefore my gift to you is the gift of my enriching company. That is sufficient return for your humble offerings."*

If that's not a message you want to send, no matter how obliquely, then keeping track of favours and thoughtfulnesses on the part of friends and keeping them in balance will make our relationships more comfortable. Virtue is its own reward, but deep down we all want recognition of some sort for the good that we do, and sometimes a simple 'thank you' is enough to level the balance.

3

IF keeping a balance in our transactions with others makes our world a little more comfortable, it's also true that keeping a balance within our own lives is equally important. Every person has three lives: a public life, a private life and a secret life. No one of these three should be allowed to dominate; an individual who allows that to happen finds his life out of balance.

In this increasingly secular society, many of the old certainties are disappearing. The once blind faith that we had in the Church, the government and the propriety of big business is fast eroding with every new revelation and every new tribunal. We put our faith more and more into the material world of possessions and consumerism because it holds certainty. The credo becomes 'money buys you what you want', and therefore pursuit of money means you'll have everything you want. To a degree it's a tempting model, but look well at anyone you know who's made the pursuit of money an end in itself. It doesn't make for a well-rounded individual. Just as a hobby can turn into an obsession, so devotion to only one aspect of our lives becomes obsessive when it's to the exclusion of all else.

Somewhere in the journey there has to be time to stop and smell the flowers. As a devout atheist, my version of spirituality is not a Christian one, yet it exists. Watching the unfolding of the seasons, hearing a vixen's cry, watching a kingfisher dive, an ant carrying a crumb of bread – these things still fill me with wonder. And it's that sense of wonder at the myriad strategies that life employs to ensure its grip on perpetuity that makes me know that I'm alive and that, despite its infinite vastness, there's a sense of belonging in the enormity of the universe.

4

I MENTIONED yesterday my atheist cast of mind. It started
I suppose with reading the Scottish philosopher David Hume
in my late teens. His wish, and that of many subsequent phi-
losophers, has been to construct a worldview that was based
purely on reason and observable phenomena. It's an aspira-
tion that I'd also subscribe to, and yet even devotees of this path
find themselves with views that can only be based on faith.

I believe, for example, that the universe that we inhabit is teem-
ing with life. I believe that life is the rule, not the exception. And
yet where is my proof? Inductive reasoning brings me to that
conclusion, but there isn't one iota of evidence that I could point
to in order to support that belief. When I read about black holes
in the fabric of space, what can I take as evidence for their existence? The fact that they help to explain the observed celestial
phenomena makes them tempting – it's a solution for the puz-
zle of where all the missing matter can be. It's tidy and it fits the
quantum theory. But is that in itself a reason to accept it?

Before the advent of the Renaissance we had a flat earth – a disc
that hung somehow in the middle of celestial spheres. With
this Aristotelian model you could explain all observed phenomena, from the daily rising of the sun to the motions of the plan-
ets. It was tidy and fitted the facts. For 1,500 years it was de-
fended with rigour; to question it was tantamount to heresy and
risked death at the stake. Today we know the model to be wrong.

Each new discovery brings revisions of the old theories, a new
assemblage of the accepted facts. As a race, we learn as we go
along, just as we do individually.

5

"*C*ERTAINTY," said Ambrose Bierce, *"is being mistaken at the top of one's voice."* Opinions and beliefs are things that many of us hold dear – we have a history full of people prepared to undergo torture and even death rather than alter their beliefs. Politicians think that the greatest public sin that they can commit is to change their minds.

But here's the thing – how would it be if we all still held the same beliefs that we held when we were five? One of the prime requisites of intelligence is adaptation – learning from one's environment and adapting accordingly. There's a case for treating opinions like stamp collectors treat their hobby. You keep a stamp until you can get your hands on one in better condition. You could try holding on to an opinion until you hear a better one. Discard the old, adopt the new. Actually we go through this process much of the time, trying out new versions of the truth of events and nature. But there's always a kernel that we call our 'deeply held beliefs' that we're unwilling to change.

Why this is so is probably more to do with security than logic. Our religion is most often that of our parents. We inherit the belief system just as we inherit our genes. It's a package of beliefs that comes with a bundle of sociological and historical taboos and shibboleths – it forms a big piece of our cultural identity. Changing these beliefs becomes as big a step as changing your passport for that of another nation. There's a suspicion that by doing so you're selling out your heritage.

But your search for truth is a never-ceasing one. Once you accept the infinity of the universe, then no terrestrial truth can hold any validity other than its curiosity value. And that's a thought that will either scare you or excite you.

DICK WARNER

1

I STAYED for a couple of weeks on La Gomera recently. It's one of the smaller Canary Islands and tourist development is only beginning. I stayed in an apartment that I rented from an old man. He had a large and beautiful garden in which he grew bananas and papayas and guavas and tomatoes and peppers, as well as decorative things like bougainvilleas and wonderful climbing geraniums.

At one time his terraces of garden had been his livelihood. He had sold the produce to rear his family. But the Canary Islands have a complicated relationship with the European Union that has ended up wrecking their agriculture and horticulture. So my landlord had to build three small apartments on his precious terraces to keep the family going.

I watched him every day. He was out there watering and weeding and pruning and the strong sun had wrinkled his skin like a lizard's. He loved his garden and he hated his apartments. He was not really happy with the way the island was going. And I thought to myself – something rather like this is going to happen in Ireland. I wonder if we'll end up like that old Gomeran man, hating what our new-found prosperity is forcing us to do?

2

ONE of the most extraordinary things about life in the 21st century is the amount of time we all spend living in artificial microclimates. The temperature around us is a matter of choice – either our choice or somebody else's – and often so is the humidity and the ventilation. This happens in our homes, our cars, our offices, and places like shops and banks and pubs. One of the fashionable names for the phenomenon is 'climate control' – a strange and rather arrogant name.

I grew up in a world where there was a much closer relationship between the weather outside and the weather inside. It was a world of draughty houses and open fires, of cars which had heaters as optional extras, of schools where we all fought to sit on a clanking cast-iron radiator during winter breaktimes. It was a much, much less comfortable world.

But today I'm feeling a little nostalgic about it because spring is happening on the far side of the double-glazing. An Irish spring is not a very comfortable thing. It's full of rain and wind and frost. But it is exciting. It's full of new growth and new life and the promise that there might even be a decent bit of summer this year. And I feel a bit resentful that I am being kept away from all this excitement by the people who want my climate to be controlled.

3

I WAS in a fishing-tackle shop the other day, buying a few bits and pieces and chatting to the owner. If you're not a fisherman I should explain that, if you go into a good fishing-tackle shop, you have to allow a minimum of 45 minutes for the most basic purchase. They are one of the last places in the world where total strangers fall into instant and meaningful conversation with each other.

But the conversation I had with the owner of this shop was not a happy one. He was in bad humour. *"The trade in fishing tackle is declining steadily,"* he explained. And it wasn't just his shop. He was a wholesaler as well and he claimed that the same thing was happening all over the country. I was surprised. I had assumed that leisure activities like fishing would be booming in our new, more affluent society. It must be, I guessed, because our water quality is deteriorating and our fish stocks are declining. *"No,"* he said. *"It's because everyone is working a lot harder and they don't have the time for things like fishing."* I was shocked. What a reflection on modern life if people no longer have the time to go fishing.

It was only after I'd left the shop that it occurred to me that I was doing less fishing than ever, and the reason was that I could no longer find the time.

4

I DON'T think I've ever met anyone who disliked trees. Everybody seems to have positive feelings about them and some people love them passionately. This is a universal phenomenon. What happened recently in the Glen of the Downs has also happened in the United States, in northern India and Kenya. I'm curious about what it is about trees that makes them evoke these feelings. Why do we all like what are, after all, just large plants?

There are three things I can think of about the average tree that make it a particularly attractive symbol of the natural world. The first is a negative thing – trees are, by and large, non-threatening. This is not true of other aspects of nature, which many of us seem to find challenging or even frightening. The second is positive – trees are passive. They don't move about the place – and so they're very peaceful. The third is connected to this – trees are mostly very much larger than we are. So we have a living thing which is very large and very passive and very non-threatening – a sort of monster teddy-bear of the vegetable world. Very hard to dislike, really.

5

I WAS invited to tea in a farm kitchen the other day. Part of the meal was a delicious, hot apple-tart. The farmer apologised for the fact that, although he had a quota to milk 70 dairy cows, he had no cream to go with the apple-tart.

This is one of the ways in which Irish life has changed in a generation, almost without our noticing it. Not so long ago, the average family produced at least a proportion of the food they ate. Today that's almost disappeared. In fact much of what we eat comes from countries most of us have never visited. This has some advantages. One obvious one is that the distance between the producer and the consumer has made food safety such an important consideration that we now have to have a whole commission of the European Union devoted to it.

Another, less obvious, disadvantage is that we have lost the immense satisfactions to be gained from producing our own food. Anyone who has carried freshly dug spuds into the kitchen, collected eggs from under the hen or even picked wild mushrooms will know what I mean. That kind of food nourishes more than the body – it also satisfies the soul.

MIKE WATTS

1

IN the mid-1950s, a man emerged from a state psychiatric hospital in Australia after a severe and prolonged mental illness. From being a highly acclaimed priest and teacher with doctorates in philosophy and divinity he was now classed as a paranoid schizophrenic, barely able to cope with the role of curate in a small country parish. He had a huge sense of stigma – a fear and sense of shame in the company of others. One Sunday at mass he decided to share his experiences with the congregation. To his surprise and relief, he was met with understanding, warmth and acceptance.

Con Keogh was to go on to become a co-founder of a worldwide mental health movement known as GROW. Its early members soon realised that the greatest key to mental health is friendship. Today, in Ireland, on the other side of the world, in a time when money and opportunity often seem to be spilling from the trees, there is a growing recognition that mental breakdown can happen to anyone. It is a time when suicide is a huge stark reality, especially among the young. Maybe it is a time for all of us to turn our minds and hearts to the inestimable value and mystery of friendship. Maybe within friendship lies the key to life, to this day with all its cares, joys and opportunities. Maybe this day holds the key to tomorrow.

2

YEARS ago, before the time of mental hospitals or the concept of community care, people who became seriously mentally ill were likely to be either incarcerated at home or sent off to wander the roads of Ireland. The incarceration would be in attics, if the houses were large, or in makeshift pits covered with an iron grid, if, like most, the house was small. Joe Robins, in his book *Fools and Mad*, talks of a lake in Kerry which was said to have special healing powers for anyone affected by madness, and many of those who were thrown out of, or who left, their homes made their way southwest in search of healing. In this part of Ireland one of the commonest wild flowers is the fuchsia.

Its name in Irish is *Deora Dé*, which means 'Tears of God'.

The flower of the fuchsia is like a scarlet tear. Its stem is full of honey, and children suck the blooms like clover. GROW Community Mental Health Movement in Ireland has chosen the fuchsia as a symbol of its work. Mental illness can be seen as a weeping of the soul. The red flowers of the fuchsia around the lakes of Kerry are a reminder of the hidden pain carried by so many in our society today and of the hidden sweetness of the human heart that is healed through friendship.

3

O NE of the commonest features of mental illness is isolation. In depression there is an unnatural pull to get away from people and to spend time alone. Even when you are manic, you manage to keep people away, by being so hyped up yourself that others only exist as an extension of your own elated feelings. When you are less than able to face life, because of depression or fear or pressing worries, or because of tragedy or abuse, there is often a genuine turning to God. Sometimes people justify their isolation by saying they need time to pray.

When I was a young man, and isolated, and reaching towards God, I read a book about the history of the monastery. I think I wanted to become a hermit. I was surprised to learn that hermits were selected by their communities. The few selected would be those most able to live in community and they would have had to have been doing so for a minimum of 10 years. The hermits were the most able of human beings, those who thrived and grew through the lives of their friends within the order and periods of daily solitude provided by the monastery.

It seems that, as well as the love and help of God, which is there in every breath we breathe, in every flower and field, every blade of grass and every drop of rain, we need the communion of others. Maybe we need to explore our own ability in our own community before isolating ourselves in work, in pleasure, in holidays, in sickness, in television, in food.

4

WE live in a world of *things*. All of us inundated by them. On our way to work every morning, we are surrounded by an ever-denser line of things called cars and things called buses and lorries. Every day things called bills and promotion leaflets fall through things called letterboxes. We are bombarded by things called advertisements to take things like coffee, burgers, chocolates, alcohol, perfume into or onto our bodies. In order to cope with ordinary everyday living, more and more people, it seems, take things called tranquillisers, which are little things called tablets, in order to calm them down.

There are three much more powerful tranquillisers than pills. The first is life itself. If we take time to listen, we will hear its voice. The second is the human mind and its ability to help us deal with life. As humans, each of us possesses a thing called a brain. The human brain is the most complicated thing in the known universe. All religions agree that through meditation our minds can bring us peace. The third tranquilliser is the love of another human being. There is nothing as calming or so beautiful as to experience the love or friendship of others and to be able to return that love. Things called tranquillisers are valuable when we are so broken that we cannot use our minds or respond to friends, but they are only the starting point to recovery.

5

FOUR years ago, a world conference on Mental Health held in Trinity College Dublin noted as its first conclusion that, *"Spirituality is an essential dimension of mental health, if we view mental health as more than the absence of severe distress and disorder . . . and we do."* The most important needs of all people are, when you think about it, spiritual. We all need hope, trust, understanding, perseverance, courage and encouragement, acceptance, support. None of us can supply these for ourselves without having others offer them to us. This kind of person-to-person spirituality differs from belief in God, which is a kind of vertical relationship. It is horizontal spirituality, the spirit that is nurtured and kept alive between people. The Mental Health conference went on to state that *"Spirituality has largely been lost in western bioscience, psychiatry and psychology, but remains a central concern for non-Western societies, and many citizens and users of mental health services throughout the world."*

What does my life offer to others as I live it today? Have I lost my sense of wonder? Do I see others merely as bodies that get in my way?

JENNY WHEATLEY

1

IN the misty morning, my daughter and I walked down the lane. I was in a rush. I usually am, dashing from one unfinished project to another that is important to nobody but myself. Rosie, who is two years old, held my hand. Her lifelong friend Teddy came along too. They come as a pair.

Suddenly I felt a resistance, a reluctance to follow me in my busy day. Impatiently I stopped with her. Unreasonably irritated by her curiosity, I looked around to try and see what had interrupted us, and at first I couldn't see anything that extraordinary. I have been up and down our lane so many times that every stone and blade of grass seems like an old friend. What could have caught her attention?

At last I saw it. The morning mist had caught, suspended in mid-air, a spider's web. The early morning dew layered every strand, showing off its beauty to the world.

I was glad that I had stopped. It was a miracle of creation captured for a moment. What a wonderful thing it was to see through the eyes of a child.

2

MY bathroom scales do not tell lies. This sad and grim fact I have known for a long time, but I chose not to believe them. For years now I have tweaked the little button at the back, trying to make the needle stay at absolute zero before I ventured on to them. I have shoved them around the bathroom floor with my feet, not actually kicking them, but the threat was there. Still, they truthfully show that slow gradual gain.

I have cursed them, and even threatened to throw them out, trying to persuade them to tell another happier tale. They, however, have integrity, taking their job as seriously as any court-house scales of justice. They do not cheat. They stand firm. So I have finally decided to take the blame off them and apportion it where it truly belongs, onto myself.

The bathroom scales do not lie, but I have been in denial. I can admit it now and be brave. But I wonder is that the only thing I have lied to myself about?

3

I AM the great procrastinator. *"Why do today what you can put off until tomorrow?"* is a saying that dances glibly off my tongue. However, I secretly wish to be different.

Every autumn for the past few years I have tried to change this bad habit and every autumn I have failed dismally.

We have an old apple tree that bears the most beautiful, sweet-tasting apples and while I can easily reach the lower branches to harvest them the upper branches tease me. It seems that the biggest and best are up there out of my reach. Even by going up on a ladder and risking my life I still can't reach the fruit. I always make a mental note to put a net around the base of the tree to catch the windfalls from above. Every year I forget. The October gales come and the apples fall into the undergrowth and are lost to me.

Like so many other things in life, I am thwarted, not by other people nor by external influences, but by my own failings. But I shan't give up; one year I'll get those apples. You wait and see.

4

I AM not from this country. I wasn't born here but came here as a very young child. As far back as I can go into the past of my family not many of them came from the place where they finally settled. They moved here and there to different areas, so each new generation had to come to terms with a place that didn't belong to them and where they didn't belong.

Now as an adult when I walk through the village where I live with my own little girls, I am impressed and happy to think they are walking the same pavements that I walked as a child. I hope that they will grow up feeling that they really belong here.

My people all moved by choice. They decided where to go and just went. Nobody forced them to leave their home.

The refugees of today are in a different situation. They have been blown by the storms of our times. Circumstances have scattered them around the globe. When they finally wash up on some friendly shore, they have to learn new languages or come to terms with new cultures. They may never have the chance to revisit old places and see their children walk in the streets of their own childhood. They have lost for ever their sense of belonging, that comfortable feeling that most people take for granted.

5

ILOVE all the seasons – spring, with its unfolding life and promise of things to come, wakes in me a great restlessness. The bright green leaves are early heralds of the cooling shade those trees will provide me with on those lovely, hot summer days that I always believe are going to come. Even if the summer turns out to be a wet disappointment, which it usually does, I still appreciate the long, light-filled days that allow me to do more things in the garden. I can be ready for the autumn harvest that will go some way towards feeding the family.

When autumn comes I am cheered by its warm colours on a woodland walk. Bonfires of fallen leaves scent the air and the misty smoke lingers in my clothes as I stroll through the early dusk. These evenings with their snap of cold turn my thoughts to the warmth of a cosy fire.

Winter and the naked trees reach upward to rain-filled skies. It is the time of sleep, when the natural world shuts down and lies dormant; it breathes slowly, waiting patiently for the rebirth of spring.

I love all the seasons, when I feel the pulse of nature beating through the year. It makes me glad to be alive.

MARY P WILKINSON

1

IN June the trees bend like they do in January. The white-grey sky is hungry for some blue, some glow of sun. From the window I see this – a frame of the day outside. Inside, the kitchen floor, freshly washed, dries. Small pools of water remain. The house is a silent house of the month of June. The children do not make a sound. They are dazzled by a television show that has lured them for now. They have forgotten about their bicycles thrown on their sides in the driveway; the soccer ball lost in the nettles; the sandbox I dug out of the shed and filled with white silken grains, buckets and rakes, and moulds of seahorses and starfish for their enjoyment. In June I do not wear socks. I splash my face with cold water. I make strawberry mousse with the fruit I bought on the side of the road from a child who sits there all day with a small radio in his ears. We eat some strawberries in the car. They are tangy sweet. The juice stains my white shirt. I do not care. In June it is possible to eat strawberries in your car and not care.

Soon I will tell the children it is time to go outside. When I do, the television is silent. It is warm to my touch. Beyond the window the children scatter, their skin, smooth and honeyed, is clustered with goose bumps. From the window I see this. In June it must be so.

January is another story . . . and it is in January that I come across these words. My journal of a day in June. It startles me that I have forgotten all of this and it is only because of my notes that I am able to recall the experience. How quickly it is that we forget moments and feelings, the wealth of a day in just 300 words.

2

THE nursing home was difficult to find. Up and down wind-ing country roads until we finally came upon a low-lying bungalow with a small parking lot to the front. The nurses smiled when we entered and we were told that my aunt was down the hall. Last door to the right.

The night before, we had gone through the photograph album where the black-and-white images from the thirties revealed a beautiful woman with bobbed hair, dressed in white in May poses. Happy parties by the coast, and with her uncle, the priest, in the country with the trestle tables placed on the lawn, and always my aunt radiant. On honeymoon in London, babies, graduations and weddings. A life passing. Ticking by. Every precious moment to cherish. Not to be wasted. To smile. Her smile captured on the faded pages of a photograph album.

The long corridor that ran through the nursing home led us to the door of my aunt's room, where we paused before entering.

3

A GREAT line has been placed on the ocean floor, connecting the mainland electricity to the island. Like a thick umbilical cord stealing itself through the currents bringing light to these people of the sea.

It was lunchtime when I heard about it. Suddenly the hotel dining room filled with animated weather-beaten faces. Strong, bronzed, ruddy complexions – all men, looking pleased with themselves; the first day of vacation for me and the end of this two-year project for them. Light had finally come to the island. There was every reason to celebrate.

For years the power chugged on and off, run by three generators that were unreliable at best. And now this great achievement confirmed permanent electricity, constant light. I congratulated the crew – but privately, I wondered about this, about its implications. Sure, it meant consistency and security to the islanders, but I couldn't help feeling a certain loss, a tinge of regret for things past, soon to be forgotten by that great surge coming from the mainland.

4

THIS spring I can expect my neighbour, Mary, to appear with her annual gift. I look forward to this event because I rarely see her during the long winter when daylight is precious. I may catch a glimpse of her all right, bringing feed to her cows, or filling a bucket with turf from the great stack beside her house. But as usual the horn from my car is bound to receive a brief dismissive wave before she returns once more to the pressing matters at hand.

But that all changes once spring arrives. Then my neighbour is reborn. Suddenly there is time for small talk, for great smiles, embracing waves. Life takes on a slower pace. The warmth in the sun softens everything. The outdoors becomes accessible and windows are opened, the soil dug, seeds planted. Hope is plentiful. Possibilities endless!

And one Sunday afternoon my neighbour will appear. She will ride her bicycle down the mile or so to my house and on the handlebars will be a shopping-bag full of daffodils from her garden. We will chat like old friends reunited, with scent of spring filling our nostrils, until we embrace, at the passing of another year . . .

5

THE storm blew all night and most of the day, and by noon time our household was experiencing serious cabin fever. Diversions were hastily put into place – fires lit, dinner made and that early glass of wine to placate the soul did not seem like a bad idea after all. Then, suddenly the storm broke up and out of it white towers of clouds appeared that defied description. Some of the clouds dissipated, yet others rose majestically up over the house splaying wild abstractions our way and tempting our drowsy senses.

Quick as lightning we washed up and threw sweaters, scarves, layers onto our housebound bodies to drive the 10-minute run to the beach. And all this time we studied the sky, wanting this reprieve in the winter's day to last. Light is a precious thing in November and we knew that, by 4.15 pm, darkness falls. At the ocean's side we had 30 minutes to walk and play and let the children run wild, streaking bits of coloured wool on the sand, muffled voices, sunken footprints and huge pieces of driftwood strangled in kelp like frozen sea-monsters.

For 30 minutes we screamed and yelled like mad, escaped prisoners, letting the house out of our system. Just 30 minutes. A lifetime. When at last we thought to look west, the opaque sun had already set. Our time was up.

LIST OF CONTRIBUTORS

Charlie Bird
Charlie Bird is Chief News Correspondent with RTÉ News. He has covered many of the major stories at home and abroad. In 1998, along with his colleague, George Lee, he was nominated Journalist of the Year for his work relating to financial scandals in the banking sector.

Elizabeth Carty
A native of Loch Gowna, County Cavan, Elizabeth Carty has lived in Meath since 1986 and is married with two daughters. She has received many award for her writing over the last six years. She works as a part time literary facilitator with Dunboyne Rehab Centre, County Meath.

Vincent DeVeau
Vincent DeVeau, a writer and editor, is currently editorial director of Smurfit Communications. Born in New York City, he is (a) the son of Jeanne Gerahty and Vincent DeVeau, Sr., and (b) the father of Christopher DeVeau, aged ten. His proudest achievement is being the connection between (a) and (b).

David Deegan
David Deegan is 30 years old. He lives in the Waterford countryside, having spent a number of years working in Germany and England. He now works in the Architectural Salvage area.

Katie Donovan
Katie Donovan is a poet and a journalist with *The Irish Times*. She has published three collections of poetry with Bloodaxe Books.

Bishop Martin Drennan
An Auxiliary Bishop in the Dublin diocese, with special responsibility for the area of education, Bishop Drennan has taught in St Kieran's College, County Kilkenny, in the Irish College in Rome and as professor of Sacred Scripture in St Patrick's College, Maynooth.

Paul Durcan
Paul Durcan is a poet. His new collection, *Cries of an Irish Caveman*, is published by The Harvill Press.

Anne Enright
Anne Enright was born in 1962. Her books *The Portable Virgin*, *The Wig My Father Wore* and *What Are You Like?* have won several prestigious awards. Her most recent stories have appeared in *The Paris Review* and *The New Yorker*.

Frank Feely
Frank Feely was Dublin City Manager and Town Clerk for seventeen years. He was the originator of the city's 1988 Millennium celebrations. He has presented a series of interview programmes on cable television. He is the chairman of the management committee of Our Ladies Hospital for Sick Children.

Norman Fischer
Norman Fischer is a Zen Buddhist priest and poet who served as abbot of the San Francisco Zen Centre from 1995–2000. He is founder and teacher for the Everyday Zen Foundation and author of many books.

Hayley Fox Roberts
Liverpool-born Hayley Fox Roberts is a poet, hypnotherapist and activist. As a therapist she works primarily within the queer community around issues of self-esteem. She is highly regarded for her performance poetry, and has published two volumes of poetry.

Sheena Furlong
Sheena Furlong is 20 years of age and lives in Waterford. She studied Business at Waterford Institute of technology. She has presented a programme for teenagers on RTÉ Radio 1, and hopes to pursue a career in broadcasting.

Ann Henning Jocelyn
Ann Henning Jocelyn is a Swedish-born author, playwright and translator based in Connemara. She is best known for her *Connemara Whirlwind* trilogy. *Keylines*, a collection of her contributions to *A Living Word*, was published last year by Doonreaghan Press.

Rita Ann Higgins
Rita Ann Higgins, a poet and playwright, was born and lives in Galway. She has been Writer-in-Residence for County Galway,

County Offaly and at the National University of Ireland, Galway, and has been Green Honors Professor at Texas Christian University. She has received many awards and bursaries. She is a member of Aosdána.

Rose Mary Logue
Rose Mary Logue lives in Dublin. She pursued a career in university administration until she resigned in order to pursue varied interests. She now works part-time as a free-lance administrator.

Richard Marsh
Richard Marsh is an American living in Ireland since 1980. He is a radio presenter, fiction and non-fiction writer, coffee house poet, teacher, storyteller and Legendary Tour guide. Collections of legends from County Wicklow, Spain and the Basque Country are forthcoming.

Geraldine Mills
Geraldine Mills lives in Galway with her husband and two children. She is a poet and short story writer who is published internationally. Her awards include the Hennessy/Tribune Emerging Writer Award and The New Irish Writing Award.

Seán Moncrieff
Seán Moncrieff was born in London, but moved to County Galway as a child. He now lives in Dublin with his wife and three children. He has worked as a researcher for Channel 4, and as a broadcaster with RTÉ, BBC and Channels 4 and 5. His first novel, *Dublin*, was published in May 2001 by Doubleday.

Eibhlín Nic Eochaidh
Eibhlín Nic Eochaidh lives in Glenfarne, County Leitrim, with her husband. A mother of grown-up sons, she is a member of the Knocknarea Writers' Group. She was the 1999 winner of the Patrick Kavanagh Award for an unpublished manuscript of poetry.

Rabbi Julia Neuberger
Julia Neuberger was rabbi to the South London Liberal Synagogue for 12 years. She has been involved in health care issues throughout her career. She has held fellowships at universities in Britain and the US and was the Chancellor of the University of Ulster 1994-2000. She has written books on Judaism, women's issues and health-care ethics.

Rita Normanly

Rita Normanly lives in rural South Sligo. She enjoys amateur drama, community projects, folklore and traditions. She has contributed to *Sunday Miscellany* and is a member of Knocknarea Women Writers.

Mary O'Malley

Mary O'Malley was born and lives in County Galway. She has published four collections of poetry, as well as editing two books of children's writing. She has completed residencies in Mayo and in Derry, the latter resulting in *The Waterside Book*. She has travelled widely in Europe and the US giving lectures and readings.

Joe O'Shea

Joe O'Shea is a 31-year-old native of Cork City who has been working in journalism in Dublin for over ten years. A feature writer with *The Star* newspaper, he makes occasional forays into magazine and broadcasting work.

John O'Shea

John O'Shea was a sports journalist for the Irish Press Group and founded GOAL, the third world relief and development agency. He has been its full-time director since 1994. He is married with two sons and two daughters.

Colin O'Sullivan

A native of Killarney, Colin O'Sullivan teaches in a boys' school in west London. His poetry has been published in various magazines He lived in the north of Japan for a year where he began to write short stories and prose as well as poetry. He is a member of the Fia Rua Writers' Group.

Jonathan Philbin Bowman

Jonathan Philbin Bowman (1969–2000). A journalist for the *Sunday Independent,* a broadcaster for RTÉ and a commentator.

Jack Preger

Jack Preger was born in 1930 into a Manchester Jewish family. He graduated from Oxford and farmed for eight years in Wales before studying medicine in Dublin. He has lived in India since 1972 and is the founder of Calcutta Rescue. Jack Preger has been awarded the MBE.

David Rice

David Rice directs the Killaloe Hedge-School of Writing and has been head of the Rathmines School of Journalism. His five books include *Shattered Vows*, which became the Channel 4 film *Priests of Passion*. A native of Newry, he has been Dominican priest, newspaper editor, and syndicated columnist.

Mary Rieke Murphy

Mary Rieke Murphy grew up in Jefferson City, Missouri, USA, and now lives in Dublin with her husband and three daughters. She has worked as a freelance journalist and taught in Trinity College Dublin and St Patrick's College, Drumcondra. She is editor of *Outlook* magazine. A book of her short stories will be published soon.

John W Sexton

John W Sexton is a poet, a radio scriptwriter and the creator of RTÉ's children's radio serial *The Ivory Tower*. His books include *The Prince's Brief Career* and *The Johnny Coffin Diaries*. He has also released an album, *The Sons of Shiva*.

John Seymour

John Seymour was born in England in 1914. He lived in southern and central Africa before joining the army and serving in Ethiopia and Burona. After the war he returned to England and started broadcasting and writing. He is the author of over thirty books. He now lives in County Wexford, Ireland.

Eamonn Sweeney

Eamonn Sweeney was born in Sligo in 1968 and now lives in Cork. He is the author of two novels, *Waiting for the Healer* and *The Photograph*, both published by Picador.

Colm Tóibín

Colm Tóibín was born in Enniscorthy in 1955. He is the author of three travel books and four novels, including *The Blackwater Lightship*, which was shortlisted for the Booker Prize in 1999. His books have been translated into sixteen languages.

Brian Trench

Brian Trench, a full-time journalist for over 20 years, is a lecturer in the School of Communications, Dublin City University, with special interests in science communication, social uses of technology and online journalism. He is a member of the Irish Council for Science Technology and Innovation.

Paolo Tullio

Paolo Tullio is a writer, an actor and broadcaster. He has acted on the Dublin stage and his film work includes parts in *The Butcher Boy*, *The General* and *The Tailor of Panama*. He has published three books, and he is the restaurant reviewer and wine correspondent for the *Irish Independent*.

Dick Warner

Dick Warner is a writer, broadcaster and environmentalist and has worked as a radio producer with RTÉ. He is best known as the presenter of the television documentaries *Waterways*, *Voyage* and *Spirit of Trees*. He lives with his wife and two children in County Kildare.

Mike Watts

Mike Watts is the National Co-ordinator of GROW Community Mental Health Movement. He is married and has four children. His hobbies include gardening, tin-whistle playing, painting, writing and walking. He has published *Nonsense Rhymes ... or Does it?*

Jenny Wheatley

Jenny Wheatley was born in Cornwall but now lives in County Waterford with her husband and two daughters. The family lives a simple life and is as environment friendly and self-sufficient as possible.

Mary P Wilkinson

Mary P Wilkinson returned to Ireland after thirteen years in the USA. She draws her inspiration from her children and the landscape of County Galway where she now lives. Her writing has featured on RTÉ 1, Lyric FM and in *Books Ireland*, West 47 and *The Irish Times*.